Human and Social Biology

Revision by Examination

P Gadd

B.Sc., M.Tech., M.I.Biol., F.L.S.

New Edition

First published 1975
Reprinted 1977, 1978, 1980
New Edition 1982
Reprinted 1983, 1984, 1986, 1991 (twice)

Published by THE MACMILLAN PRESS LTD
London and Basingstoke
Associated companies and representatives in Accra, Auckland, Delhi, Dublin, Gaborone, Hamburg, Harare, Hong Kong, Kuala Lumpur, Lagos, Manzini, Melbourne, Mexico City, Nairobi, New York, Singapore, Tokyo.

ISBN 0-333-32956-2

Printed in Hong Kong

Contents

Foreword

The questions in this book have been designed for 'O' level examinations in Human and Social Biology or Human Biology. However, the gradation of standards is such that the first questions in each chapter are also suitable for C.S.E. candidates.
The Singapore—Cambridge G.C.E. 'O' level multiple choice papers have had five options since December 1983. The items in this book have four options and if they were used as a group in an examination paper this could slightly reduce the reliability of the examination statistics. Between December 1982 and 1983 the change to five options appears to have had no effect, but between December 1983 and 1984 the standard deviation of scores increased by 1.76
The author was formerly Chief Examiner in Human and Social Biology for a C.S.E. board. He is Chief Examiner and Moderator for 'A' level Social Biology and sets external papers in Human Biology and Social Biology for 'O' level candidates. He has been responsible for training teachers in the developing countries to mark Human and Social Biology scripts and he has been involved with Health Science and Human and Social Biology examinations in several capacities over many years. He is chairman of a panel of item writers for an 'O' level multiple choice question bank.

The Nature of Examinations

1

Introduction

In spite of some critics of the examination system, many teachers spend a considerable amount of time preparing pupils to pass examinations. This book is intended to help teachers in this task by giving a supply of questions which serve at the same time to act as a revision programme. Possibly most teachers accept examinations as a useful aid in that they provide a stimulus which encourages pupils with their work. While we probably all agree that working through sheer interest is most desirable, this book has been written in the belief that the modern methods of examination also encourage pupils to take an interest.

Some of the new style questions aim to test aspects of a candidate's ability, other than a good memory. The ability to deduce information from facts presented; to interpret graphs or sets of figures; to select the best answers and to design experiments, are all tested by the most up to date examinations. This does not mean that factual recall questions, including questions requiring essay type answers are to be neglected. However, the best assessment of a candidate's abilities is obtained if all these types of question are used so that a variety of skills are measured. The emphasis has moved more towards a testing of understanding, rather than testing straightforward memory work. Thus the objectives of the test questions have been carefully considered, although apart from this brief mention here, their formulation is beyond the scope of this book. They mainly conform to the objectives stated in Bloom's, Taxonomy of Educational Objectives, on which much recent work in the objectives of science education is based. In addition, these questions have been designed to cover the most important points on the syllabus and so provide a useful revision course and help candidates in answering all types of examination questions.

Examination hints for teachers

In preparing pupils for examinations, it may help if you appreciate the reasons for the inclusion of certain types of question and how they are marked. We can group questions into a number of main types as follows, although you will notice in later sections that considerable overlap can occur.

Essay type

Example: Give an account of the part played by hormones in the process of reproduction in the human body.
You are probably most familiar with this traditional type of question. Such a question requires the facts to be organised in a logical order, with proper sentence construction and use of paragraphs. Such answers should have a good introduction and conclusion, and should generally be illustrated with diagrams wherever these serve to clarify the answer. Such questions encourage imagination, expression and the ability to put facts together in a readable manner.

Essay answers are usually marked from a scheme which lists the facts needed and requires the examiner to place a tick alongside the relevant fact. The most common mistake made by pupils is to give facts which are not relevant. As an illustration of this point, let us look at part of an answer to the question 'How is a constant body temperature maintained in man'? Here is an example of a poor answer.

A constant body temperature is maintained in man so that all the chemical reactions occuring in the body work efficiently. Many such reactions occur in his liver such as de-amination and the oxidation of fats. Man is uncomfortable in temperatures below 15°C. and above 40°C. If he is very hot, or very cold he cannot think clearly and.....

Now although much of the information given in the answer is correct, it does not answer this particular question and so the candidate scores 0. This answer does not tell us *how* a constant body temperature is maintained.
Now here is an example of a high scoring answer.

A constant body temperature is maintained in man because heat is generated by the process of respiration ✓ in the cells ✓ of the body. Other metabolic actions such as those occuring in the liver ✓ will also produce heat. Shivering ✓ and other muscle action assist in the production of heat.

Cooling the body is assisted by the evaporation of sweat ✓ which takes latent heat from the body. When the body is overheated the dilation of capillaries ✓ in his skin occurs so that more blood passes through them bringing more heat to the surface which is lost by radiation and convection. In the cool body vaso-constriction occurs. The skin capillaries constrict so that less blood flows through them to cause heat loss

The skin also has a layer of fat which serves as an insulator retaining heat within the body. Hair may trap air and also act as an insulator, but this is more important in other mammals. Man relies on clothing to trap air and keep him warm in cool climates.

Note how the examiner looked for facts in the above answer and placed ticks above them. A typical marking scheme for this question may look like the following.

Source of heat:	Respiration/ in cells/ liver metabolism/ shivering or muscle action	4 *marks*
Retention of heat:	Fat insulation/ clothing/ explanation of vaso-constriction	3 *marks*
Loss of heat:	Explanation of vaso-dilation/ evaporation of sweat/ radiation or convection	3 *marks*

1 mark for each of the above facts. *Maximum* 10 *marks*
Bonus for good layout and expression 0, 1 *or* 2 *marks*
Total 12 *marks*

In all such questions, the examiner will of course accept alternative expressions other than those listed in the mark scheme, provided they have the same meaning.

Structured type

Structured type questions require short, clear cut answers which are usually placed in spaces on the question paper. Numerous short questions like these allow the examiner to cover a greater part of the syllabus. Marking is easier and more reliable because of the limited number of possible answers. This makes the score obtained independent of any bias on the part of the marker. The types of questions can be divided into the following main kinds, although much overlap between these kinds may occur.

Knowledge—Simple factual recall

Example: Name the light sensitive layer of the eye.
Answer: retina.
Note there is only one possible answer and the question really only tests memory.

Knowledge—Experimental recall

Example: What colour is iodine solution when added to starch?
Answer: blue or black.

This type of question requires recall of facts about experiments performed and so tests little more than memory.

Comprehension—Translation

Example: Write down two differences between a sperm and an ovum.
Answer: Any two from: sperm is motile/has a tail/distinct head/smaller/contains a Y chromosome.
The candidate needs to know about both sperm and ova and to be able to deduce differences between them. Hence not only memory is tested, but the application of knowledge to new situations. The knowledge acquired has to be **translated** to make new associations. Note that the answer requires the candidate to refer to *either* the sperm *or* the ovum. Answers such as 'larger' or 'motile' would not gain a mark on their own.

Comprehension—Interpretation

Example: Each of the four children in a family has a different type of blood group in the ABO system. What is the genotype of the parents?
Answer: AO $\times$ BO.
A knowledge of basic genetics including the term genotype, and an understanding of blood groups, has to be applied to a situation the candidate is unlikely to have met before.
Comprehension is tested because the problem has to be understood and presented in a more meaningful form. This requires **interpretation,** which involves analysing the elements of a problem and recognising their relationship and organisation.

Application

Example: An indicator is red at pH 6, yellow at pH 7 and green at pH 8. This indicator is added to a tube containing urea solution and very dilute acetic acid. Finally the enzyme urease is added. Urease breaks down urea solution into ammonia.

1 What colour will the indicator be at first?
2 What colour change will occur to the indicator?
3 What causes the colour change of the indicator in questions 1 and 2?
4 Can you think of a reason why urease is not found in the blood of mammals?

Answers:

1 Red.
2 Red→yellow→(green).
3 Acetic acid makes the solution red in 1.
Urease breaks down the urea to ammonia, which forms an alkaline solution turning the indicator yellow then green.
4 Blood contains urea, which if it was converted to ammonia by urease would poison the body.

This answer requires application because it needs the selection of known principles to a situation, where *thought is first needed about which principle should be used.* The candidate is unlikely to have met urease before, but should have a knowledge of how other enzymes work. Using this knowledge together with a knowledge of basic chemistry the problem can be solved. Part 4 of the question is almost certain to be original, but because the average candidate should know that urea is present in the blood and that ammonia is toxic, they should be able to deduce the answer. This is a useful question because the answers are progressively more difficult and show a gradation from knowledge, through comprehension to application.

Analysis

Example: Two very similar towns A and B, initially lacked open surface water sources. Town A adapted an underwater supply, to make open irrigation canals for crops, so greatly increasing the farm production. At the same time a programme of mosquito control was successfully completed. These events coincided with an increase in the incidence of anaemia in town A, which did not increase significantly in town B, in spite of receiving visitors from town A.

1 Why was a programme of mosquito control needed in town A?

2 Explain with reasons based on the information given, which disease could have caused the increase of anaemia in town A.

Answers:

1 The irrigation channels could provide breeding grounds for the mosquitoes so increasing their numbers.

2 Bilharzia (schistosomiasis) or hookworm, caught by contact with the larvae in infected water, causes anaemia.

Application is required in this problem, but additionally analysis is needed *to sort out the relevant from the irrelevant data* provided. In this question the increased farm production is not really relevant except perhaps to make nutritional anaemia unlikely. The candidate has to rule out mosquito transmitted diseases such as malaria, as well as eliminate diseases which could be passed on in this situation by travellers. In short, the candidate must review the variety of information, select that which is most significant and put forward an acceptable hypothesis. In this respect, evaluation of the information, followed by synthesis in the formation of the hypothesis, is testing the highest skills as outlined in Bloom's Taxonomy of Educational Objectives.

Deductive type questions involve the setting of problems which candidates have to solve. Thus in nature they are often more comparable with the kind of activity the students will undertake later on in life. Memory work is reduced but other skills such as understanding, evaluating and analysing facts are important. Surely these objectives are to be preferred to the regurgitation of memorised facts so prevalent in earlier examinations?

Multiple choice

Example of a simple completion item:

Stem The tube connecting the kidney to the bladder is called the

Responses
- *Distractors*
  - A aorta
  - B tubule
  - C urethra
- *Key*
  - D ureter

Answer: D

Multiple choice questions are designed to test certain skills in the same way as we have seen for the structured questions. The example above only tests knowledge. The following example tests application.

Example of a simple completion item testing application:

A food when boiled with Millons reagent turned red and when boiled with Benedicts (or Fehling's) solution it did not change colour. We can deduce that this food contains the chemicals

A reducing sugar but not protein.

B protein but not non-reducing sugar.

C non-reducing sugar but not protein.

D protein but not reducing sugar.

Answer: D

The candidate must apply a knowledge of food tests in an unfamiliar situation.

Simple completion item testing analysis

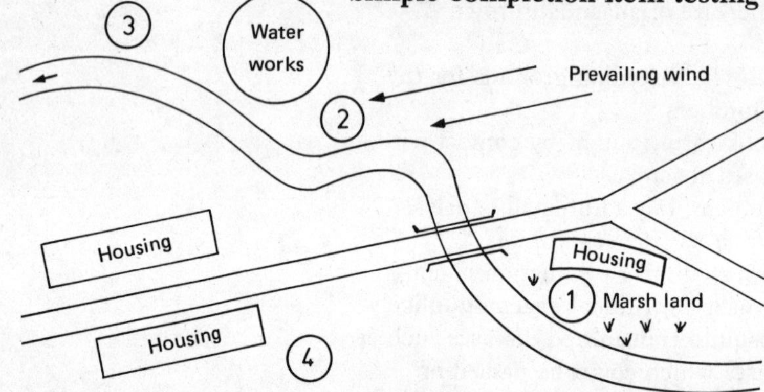

Examine the map of the town. Which of the following places would be the best site for a sewage works.

A site 1

B site 2

C site 3

D site 4

Answer: C

The candidate must consider the position of the sewage works in relation to many factors, e.g. prevailing wind, water flow, distance from water, water works and housing, and choose the best position.

Example of a classification set item:

Place the letter from the following names beside the numbered definition to which it applies below.

A respiration B photosynthesis C excretion D irritability

1 The manufacture of sugars in plants from CO_2 and H_2O

2 The ability of an organism to respond to a stimulus

3 The elimination of metabolic waste from the body

4 The release of energy from glucose in cells

Answer: 1 B 2 D 3 C 4 A. 1 mark each to a possible total of 4.

There are other varieties of multiple choice question which can be set and some of these are used later. They all involve the candidate selecting an answer from a number of alternatives. Experience seems to show that four or five alternatives are the best number to reduce the element of guessing, while still allowing suitable distractor answers to be thought out by the examiner. Such questions take a longer time to set and should be pre-tested on a group of similar children to ensure their validity. Banks of such tested questions are often stored for future use. Many of the structured type of questions we have seen so far could also be set in multiple choice form. These questions are easy to mark but very difficult to set and they test the ability to select, thus again reducing the memory element. Guessing is often said to be a disadvantage of such questions. However, it is likely that *completely* random guesses are rare. The candidate may think he has guessed but in fact he is likely to have chosen his answer at least in the light of some glimmer of past experience. It may be that such judgement is also worth rewarding.

Examination hints for candidates

Some of the following hints may seem obvious to you. Nevertheless it is surprising how many candidates lose marks because they do not follow this advice. Remember these points when you next take an examination.

Essay type questions

1 Always read the question carefully and think about it before writing your answer. Keep checking that you are answering this question. Misreading questions and writing non-relevant parts to answers are perhaps the most common of all the errors made in examinations.
2 It sometimes helps to rough out a quick plan of your answer first.
3 Divide your time equally between the number of questions asked. (Unless there are compulsory questions where you will have to make your own judgement on timing.) The first few marks on any question are usually easier to obtain. Consequently, it pays to attempt that 'last' question even if you do not know as much about it as the others.
4 Do not keep repeating facts. Each relevant fact generally gains one mark, so that repetition only wastes your time. Quality rather than quantity is important.
5 Diagrams should help clarify your answer where relevant. They are not to be used as a decoration, so do not put them in unless they serve a purpose.

6 If experiments are to be described, then give full details so that your instructions could be followed by somebody repeating your experiment. You may assume this person has a basic knowledge of science apparatus. Adopting the form in which specific apparatus is described along with the method, result and conclusion is often best. In your revision, numerical results very rarely have to be learned although the interpretation of such results may be needed.

Objective type questions

7 The amount of space left for the answer generally gives an indication of the length of answer expected. Do not try and squeeze in a lot of detail.
8 Obey the instructions fully. For instance do not indicate two answers in multiple choice questions if you are only asked for one. Should you make a mistake then delete it, for providing your intention is clear to the examiner, he will credit you with the mark, if the fact is correct.
9 Completely wild guesses at questions should be avoided, but if you have any idea at all, then it is better to write down something rather than leave a complete blank. In such cases it is better to answer these questions during your second time through the paper. The reasons for attempting such multiple choice questions in this way are given in the previous section.
10 In objective tests all questions may not gain equal marks, so it is best to work through the paper quickly, but in your own time, and then return to those parts giving you difficulty.

All types of questions

11 Be as specific as you can with words. For instance if you know a particular part is the ileum in an answer, then do not call it the small intestine. As another example, do not use terms like germs or micro-organisms if you know that the particular organism is a bacterium or a virus etc.
12 If the question asks you to compare two items then a separate description of each will not do. Points of similarity or difference should be made by reference to each item.
13 Diagrams often lose marks because guide lines are not clear, headings are missed out, parts are inaccurately placed, or the shape is wrong. Do not waste time colouring diagrams.
14 Look at the wording of questions carefully. For instance, if a question asks you to name the organ which perceives light, then an answer of the retina is an incorrect answer. If you look at the question again you will notice the word 'organ' is used. The retina is a tissue so the correct answer is, of course, the eye, which is an organ.
15 Finally, remember the examiner only wants to find out how much you know, understand and can work out. Examiners do not set trick questions, and they certainly do not want to mislead you in any way. They are much happier if you do well and pass.

The Activities, Classification and Evolution of Organisms

2

Look at the list of words (A–F) and phrases (1–11) below. Pair off the phrase with the word which you think describes it best. The first one is done for you.

A irritability
B excretion
C growth
D nutrition
E reproduction
F secretion

1 the ingestion, digestion and assimilation of food (Answer 1 D)
2 an increase in size or weight
3 elimination of metabolic waste products from the body
4 the power to respond to a stimulus
5 production of new individuals of the same species
6 passage of a useful substance made in a cell to the surroundings
7 the production of sweat for cooling the body
8 the production of urine
9 photosynthesis in plants
10 the movement of a plant's roots towards water
11 the breathing out of air rich in carbon dioxide

12 The best definition of Social Biology is the study of
A the structure and function of the human body.
B the structure of human societies and their interaction.
C the biological aspects of how man affects other men, other organisms and his environment.
D the effect of disease, population growth and pollution in human societies.

13 All living organisms are capable of the process of
A locomotion.
B photosynthesis.
C asexual reproduction.
D excretion.

14 The building up processes which occur in the body are called
A catabolism.
B catalysm.
C anabolism.
D metabolism.

15 Physiology is the study of
A the internal structure of organisms.
B the external form of organisms.
C the physical features of organisms.
D the chemical and physical processes in organisms.

16 Which of the following features distinguish mammals from other vertebrates?

A a notochord.
B pentadactyl limb.
C sweat glands.
D internal fertilisation.

In the following questions (17–20) choose the alternative which best completes the statement.

17 **Least** important in man's evolution has been
A an enormously developed fore-brain.
B his large size.
C the possession of vocal cords.
D an opposable thumb.

18 The mechanism of evolution does **not** depend on
A the production of large numbers of offspring.
B variation among individuals.
C survival of the fittest.
D the slow growth of organisms.

19 Which of the following is **not** a kind of division of labour.
A the parts of the body performing the same function.
B the parts of the body specialised to perform different functions.
C when termites divide the tasks between different members of the colony.
D the sharing of tasks between different members of the community.

20 Which of the following does not cause pollution?
A washing powders.
B motor cars.
C growing trees.
D sewage disposal.

Study the following graph in Fig. 1 and then answer the following questions (21 to 31).

21 Write down the approximate ages at points A, B and C.

Fig. 1

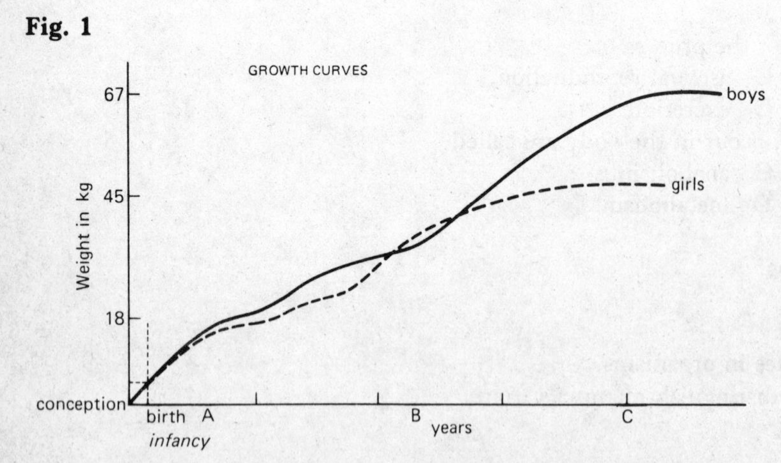

22 What is the stage of growth called between A and B?

23 What is the stage of growth called between B and C?

24 What measurement other than weight could show growth?

25 What class of food is particularly important for growth?

26 State two differences between the growth in boys and in girls which can be deduced from the graph.

27 What could account for a very slight reduction in height after point C?
28 What is the name for the period between conception and birth?
29 Name two factors which could limit growth.
30 Name the process which occurs at conception.
31 Name one developmental feature occuring between stage B and C in males, which does not occur in females.

The words in italics are the answers to statements 32 to 42. Write down the question number with the correct word beside it.
Darwin Linnaeus Schistosoma hookworm Proconsul
arthropods vertebrates phylum species bacterium fungi
32 a group of organisms which closely resemble one another, mate with others of the same kind and have young of the same type
33 the scientist who produced a theory of evolution
34 the scientist who introduced a binomial system of classification
35 a possible ancestor of man and apes
36 a group of organisms which all conform to the same basic structure
37 a microscopic one-celled organism without a distinct nucleus
38 plants which lack chlorophyll and absorb organic food
39 animals with jointed limbs and a hard external skeleton
40 a roundworm found in the small intestine
41 flatworm found in the veins supplying the liver
42 animals with backbones

Fig. 2

trypanasome (0.002cm)

sea anemone (6cm)

earthworm (15cm)

locust (8cm)

frog

Study the organisms in Fig. 2 and using these examples, answer questions 43 to 53.
43 Name one invertebrate.
44 Name one vertebrate.
45 What is the essential difference between invertebrates and vertebrates?
46 What main feature shows that *Trypanosoma* is a Protozoan?
47 Give one reason why the frog is classified as an amphibian.
48 Explain briefly which of these organisms causes the most damage to crops, and how it does so.
49 Explain briefly which of these organisms causes the most damage to health and how it does so.
50 Explain briefly which of these organisms is most useful to man, and why it is so.
51 All these drawings are of poikilothermic animals. What does this term mean?
52 Name three different kinds of locomotory organs shown in these drawings.
53 Is the sea anemone a plant or an animal? Give one reason for your answer.

Fill in the gaps in the following sentences with the best words to complete them. Write down the number of the gap with the word beside it.
Living things can be compared with machines such as the motor car because the process of combustion is somewhat similar to **54.** The filling of the car with petrol can be compared with **55** and the passing out of exhaust gases can be compared with **56.** However, unlike organisms, the motor car cannot **57** or **58.** Plants differ from animals because they take in inorganic substances and build them up into complex **59** substances, using the green pigment **60** and energy from **61.** This process is called **62** and the inorganic substances are mineral salts, water and **63.**

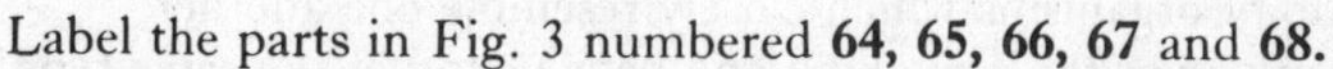

Label the parts in Fig. 3 numbered **64, 65, 66, 67** and **68.**

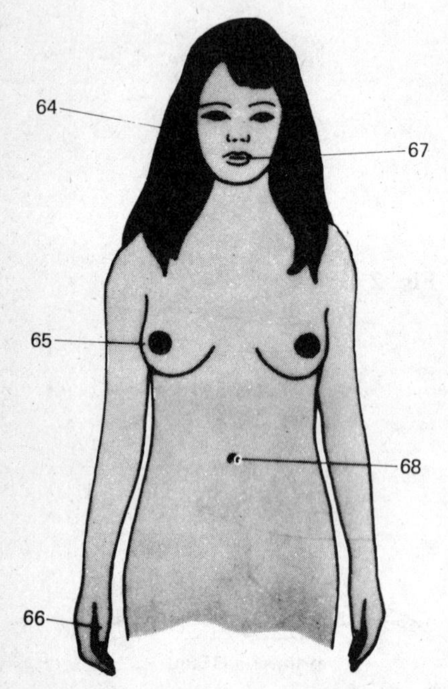

Fig. 3

69 What is the function of the part numbered 64?
70 What is the function of the part numbered 67?
71 In which particular group of animals are the numbered parts 64, 65 and 68 characteristically found.
72 Name two other characteristics common to this group of animals.
73 What is the function of the part numbered 65?
74 What is the advantage of the bipedal habit in man?
75 Man educates his young for a much longer period of time compared to any other group of animals. What two mammalian features particularly have led to this behaviour.

Evolution is a process which has taken place very slowly over many years. During this time, complex organisms have evolved from simpler ancestors. We have evidence of this from many sources including fossils. Unfortunately, few fossils of man have been found although *Homo erectus* must have been similar to such ancestors. Physically, man has evolved very little since the Stone Age.

The above paragraph is to refresh your memory with regard to evolution. Answer questions 76–81 which require additional knowledge.
76 Give an estimate of the time span since life was first believed to have originated in the ancient oceans.
77 Write down the following animals in order of increasing structural complexity. Housefly, frog, fish, bird, amoeba, mammal, tapeworm, reptile.
78 Name two parts of an animal's body likely to produce fossil remains.
79 Why were few fossils of the early ancestors of man preserved?
80 What important evolutionary change was shown by *Homo erectus* over the earlier apes?
81 If not physically, in what other way has man evolved since the Stone Age.?

Food

3

Look at the list of words (A–D) and phrases (1–15) below. Pair off each phrase with the word which you think describes it best. A word may be used more than once.

A butter
B starch
C protein
D kilojoule

1 a food rich in fat
2 a food rich in vitamin A
3 a food important for body growth and repair
4 an example of a complex carbohydrate
5 an example of a complex polysaccharide
6 a common carbohydrate stored in plants
7 the SI unit of energy
8 food containing carbon, hydrogen, oxygen, and nitrogen
9 the energy content of food is sometimes given in these units
10 soya beans, meat and yeast provide a rich source
11 a food rich in vitamin D
12 a substance composed of amino acids
13 a food highly rich in energy
14 a food rich in a substance containing carbon and hydrogen with a very small proportion of oxygen
15 kwashiorkor is caused by a diet lacking this

16 Proteins are valuable in the diet because they
A are the best source of energy.
B contain amino acids for respiration.
C are the best growth compounds.
D are the main source of vitamins.

17 The basic metabolic rate for an average man would be about
A 50 kJ.
B 100 kJ.
C 250 kJ.
D 500 kJ.

18 500 kJ is approximately equivalent to
A 60 kCal.
B 120 kCal.
C 180 kCal.
D 240 kCal.

19 A deficiency of iodine in the diet causes
A rickets.
B anaemia.
C dermatitis.
D goitre.

20 Expectant mothers require foods rich in calcium to prevent
A disease of the nervous system.

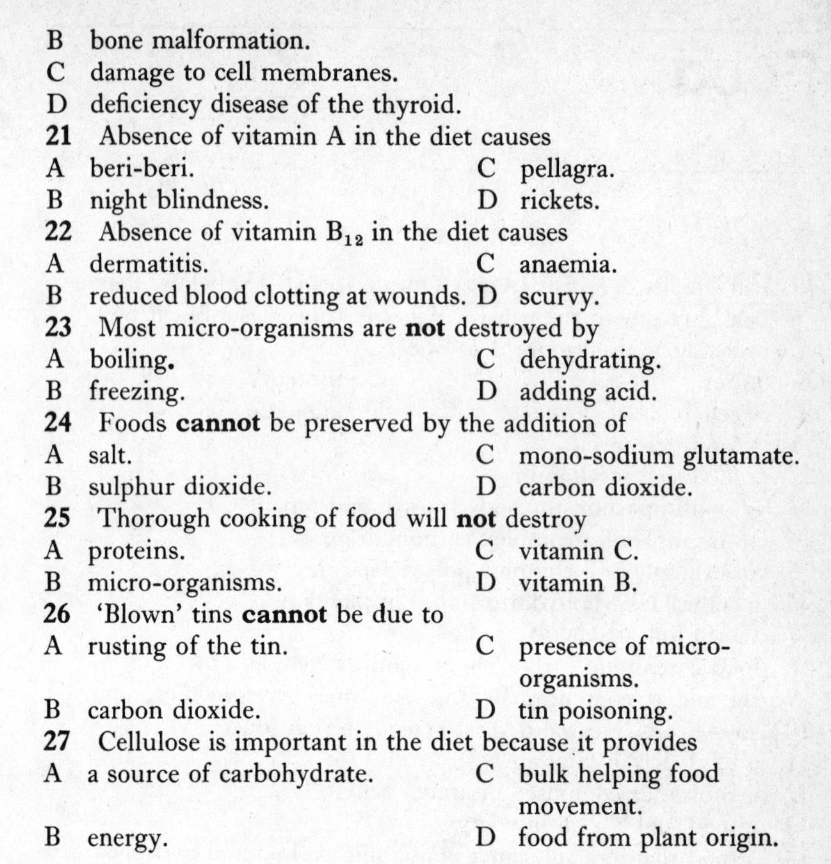

B bone malformation.
C damage to cell membranes.
D deficiency disease of the thyroid.

21 Absence of vitamin A in the diet causes
A beri-beri. C pellagra.
B night blindness. D rickets.

22 Absence of vitamin B_{12} in the diet causes
A dermatitis. C anaemia.
B reduced blood clotting at wounds. D scurvy.

23 Most micro-organisms are **not** destroyed by
A boiling. C dehydrating.
B freezing. D adding acid.

24 Foods **cannot** be preserved by the addition of
A salt. C mono-sodium glutamate.
B sulphur dioxide. D carbon dioxide.

25 Thorough cooking of food will **not** destroy
A proteins. C vitamin C.
B micro-organisms. D vitamin B.

26 'Blown' tins **cannot** be due to
A rusting of the tin. C presence of micro-organisms.
B carbon dioxide. D tin poisoning.

27 Cellulose is important in the diet because it provides
A a source of carbohydrate. C bulk helping food movement.
B energy. D food from plant origin.

Fig. 4

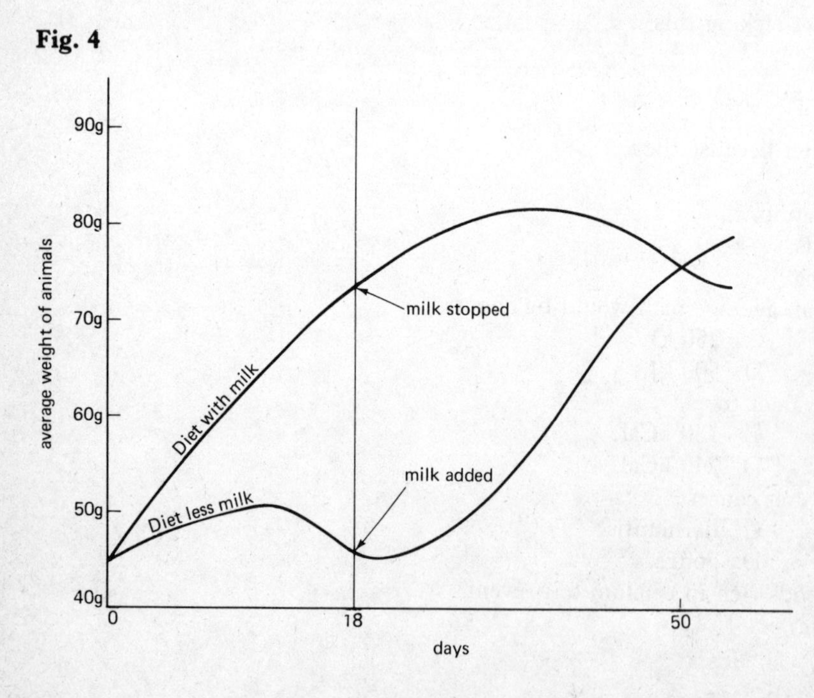

Fig. 4 shows the results of feeding young rats on a diet of *either* milk *or* sucrose, casein, lard, starch, salts and water.

28 What general conclusion can you deduce from the information given?

29 What causes the results shown on the graph?

30 How do you know that these results are not due to a lack of protein in the diet?

31 Name **one** element necessary for the formation of blood cells that is not present in milk.

32 Name **one** vitamin not present in milk.

33 Name the scientist who first reported performing these experiments.

34 Name two diseases which would occur in a man limited to such a diet without milk, as in the previous experiment.

In questions 35 to 39 write down the letter in front of the alternative which is least rich in the nutrient mentioned in each question.

35 Proteins are plentiful in

A meat. C jam.
B fish. D eggs.

36 Fats are plentiful in

A butter. C lard.
B fish. D margarine.

37 Carbohydrates are plentiful in

A bread. C liver.
B potatoes. D honey.

38 Iron is plentiful in

A liver. C milk.
B yeast. D egg yolk.

39 Vitamin C is plentiful in

A oranges. C limes.
B green vegetables. D cheese.

Refer to the drawing of the wheat grain in Fig. 5 before answering the questions 40 to 50.

40 What is the name given to part A?
41 What happens to parts A and C during milling?
42 What is the vitamin contained in parts A and C?
43 What deficiency disease results from the loss of this vitamin?
44 What other important nutrient is plentiful in parts A and C?
45 What nutrient is plentiful in part B?
46 Where was the food which is found in part B produced?
47 What process was responsible for the manufacture of the food found in part B?
48 What common tropical grain food is so similar to wheat that the answers to the above questions would have been the same?
49 How can this tropical grain food be treated to prevent loss of nutrients during its preparation?
50 Why are nutrients lost if such foods are cooked in water for long periods?

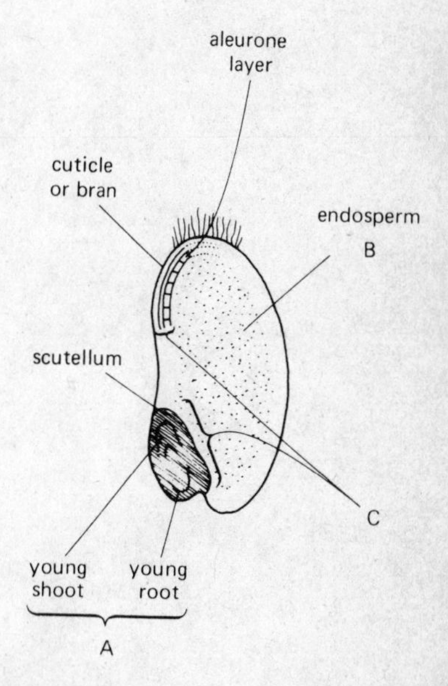

Fig. 5

Read the account of the following experiment, and then answer question 51.

A food sample turned iodine solution blue/black in colour, and when it was heated with either Fehling's or Benedict's solution it produced a red precipitate. Its colour did not change when it was heated with Millon's reagent, neither did the food sample leave a translucent mark when rubbed onto filter paper.

51 State four facts that you can deduce about the presence or absence of nutrients from these experiments.

Read the account of the following experiment and then answer questions 52 to 55.

A food heated with Fehling's or Benedict's solution did not reduce these solutions forming a red colour unless it was first boiled with hydrochloric acid and then neutralised with sodium hydroxide.

52 What kind of nutrient was present?
53 What kind of food has been proved not to be present?
54 What was the effect of the hydrochloric acid on the food?
55 How do you show that the acid is neutralised?

In questions 56 to 64 state the nutrient required in a diet to cure a child suffering from

56 anaemia.
57 rickets.
58 goitre.
59 kwashiorkor.
60 night blindness.
61 dermatitis.
62 beri-beri.
63 pellagra.
64 scurvy.

Read the account of the following experiment and then answer questions 65 to 74.
Meat broth was placed in 6 test tubes each of which was boiled and treated as follows.

A sealed with an air tight plug
B acetic acid added
C common salt added
D evaporated to dryness
E placed in a refrigerator
F tube left open

65 In which tube would the broth go bad?
66 What kind of organisms cause food to go bad?

Complete the following table by naming a commercial method of food preservation and a common food preserved for each of the test tubes from A to D above.

tube	method of preservation	name of food preserved
A	**67**	**68**
B	**69**	**70**
C	**71**	**72**
D	**73**	**74**

75 What happens to the organisms in a refrigerator?
76 Why does drying prevent food from going bad?

Read the following sentence and then answer questions 77 to 81.
A balanced diet requires foods for body building, energy expenditure and the prevention of deficiency diseases.
Write one sentence to explain the important considerations to be made in planning the diet for

77 an invalid.
78 an expectant mother.
79 a vegetarian.
80 an active labourer.
81 an overweight middle-aged man.

82 Bread has about 960 kJ/g. Explain the meaning of this statement.
83 What is the meaning of basic metabolic rate?

Note the experimental results below and answer question 84.
A calorimeter was used to oxidise completely 2 g of a food sample, causing a temperature rise of 5°C in 100 cm^3 of water (this figure includes the water equivalent of the apparatus).
84 How much energy was present in the food sample (in joule per g)?

Read the following problem and answer questions 85 to 87.
A boy weighing 40 kilogrammes climbs a vertical ladder 10 metres high. His muscles are 25 per cent efficient in obtaining the energy from glucose for this process. Assume 1 g of glucose has an energy value of 16 kJ.
85 How much work is done by the boy?
86 What weight of sugar to the nearest gramme will be used in this process only?
87 Name one other process which will be using energy at the same time?

88 Why is the reheating of meat dishes dangerous?
89 Which vitamin is produced in the skin from sunlight and ergosterol?

4 Source and Supply of Food

From the alternatives listed in the following questions (1–10) select the one which best completes the statement.

1 Man is dependent on plants for a supply of

A carbon dioxide.
B water.
C hydrogen.
D oxygen.

2 A dead animal would decay if it was

A immersed in water.
B immersed in alcohol.
C placed in a refrigerator.
D autoclaved and sealed in a container.

3 Carbon dioxide is returned to the atmosphere by

A decay of humus.
B fossil formation of coal.
C photosynthesis in plants.
D transpiration in plants.

4 Plants manufacture protein using

A denitrifying bacteria.
B lysosomes in the cell.
C chemicals produced by fungi in root nodules.
D ammonium nitrate from the soil.

5 Nitrogen is replenished in the soil by the

A addition of calcium phosphate fertiliser.
B removal of weeds between crops.
C uptake of air by nitrogen fixing bacteria.
D uptake of nitrogen gas by root crops.

6 The **advantage** of crop rotation is that

A plants become accustomed to the same conditions.
B it is easier to grow the same crops each year.
C less farming implements are needed for cultivation.
D plants do not exhaust the soil of the same mineral salts.

7 Nitrogen is **absent** in

A protein.
B urine.
C ammonia.
D starch.

8 Which of the following will **not** increase the yield of food from animals?

A providing a higher than normal oxygen concentration during development.
B providing food rich in certain nutrients.
C restricting the movement of animals.
D injecting hormones.

9 Geneticists **cannot** improve the genetic stock of animals to the advantage of man by

A improving the environment in which the animals are bred.

B selecting the largest animals from litters for breeding.
C cross breeding animals with desirable characteristics.
D artificial insemination from males of good stock.

10 Man **could** increase the food available for future generations by
A using more marginal land for plant growth.
B rearing more animals than plants for food.
C using carnivorous animals as a food source.
D using inorganic food supplies.

11 Write down an example of a food chain involving four organisms in the correct order.

In questions 12 to 14 consider what feature all organisms have in common at

12 the base of a food chain
13 the second level in a food chain
14 the top level of a food chain
15 Why does man rarely rear carnivorous animals as a food source?

Fill in the gaps to complete the following sentences.
Photosynthesis involves the manufacture of **16** from **17** and **18** using the energy from **19** and the enzymes present in **20.** The gas given off during this process is **21** which animals use in the process of **22.** Plant proteins are made from **23** absorbed from the soil combined with **24.** These second class proteins lack some **25** acids often present in animal proteins.

26 Why does a plant, growing in an air tight bottle and using oxygen for respiration, not die eventually due to lack of oxygen?
27 79 per cent of the air comprises nitrogen. Briefly explain the sequence of events by which nitrogen is built up into nitrogen compounds in man.

Examine the apparatus drawn in Fig. 6 and answer the questions 28 to 33.

28 What is under the funnel?
29 What does this experiment demonstrate?
30 How is the gas tested?
31 What control should be set up?
32 What would be the effect of increasing the light intensity?
33 If the carbon dioxide content and light intensity remain constant, what could increase the rate of bubbling?

Fig. 7 shows the main parts of a sample of soil which was vigorously shaken with water.

34 Why have the particles settled in this order?
35 Name two other parts of fertile garden soil not shown in this diagram.

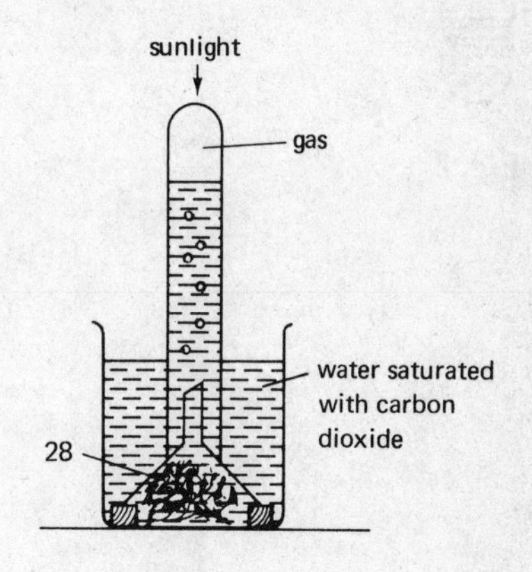

Fig. 6

Fig. 7

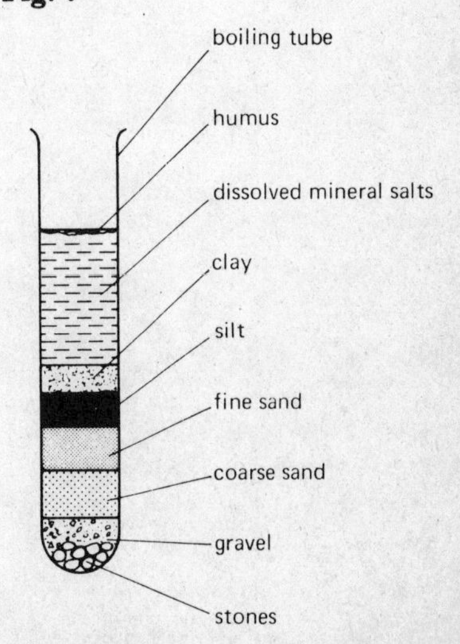

36 What is humus?
37 Why is humus important in the soil?
38 State two disadvant ıges of a sandy soil.
39 State two disadvantages of a clay soil.
40 How would the diagram in Fig. 7 differ if the soil had been shaken with limewater instead of water?
41 What is a loam soil?

Examine the apparatus drawn in Fig. 8, to show the presence of micro-organisms in the soil.

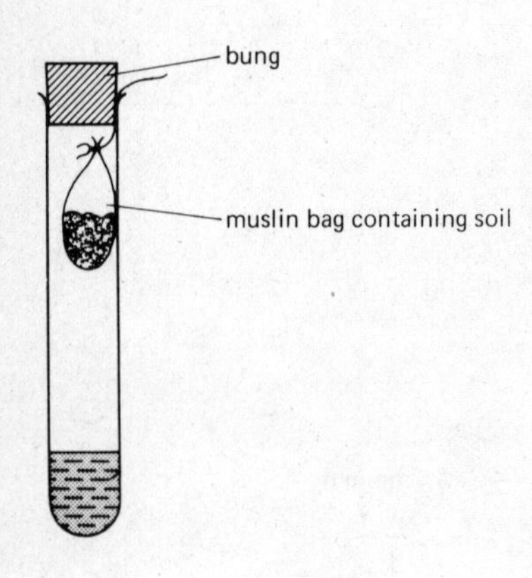

Fig. 8

42 What liquid is placed in the tube?
43 What happens to this liquid?
44 What control is needed?
45 Write down two important functions of micro-organisms in the soil.

Complete the following sentences so that they explain how the following processes damage soil fertility.

46 Cutting down forests causes.........................
47 Overgrazing by cattle causes.........................
48 Ploughing can hasten sheet erosion because.........................
49 Heavy rainfall on sandy soils causes leaching which.........................
50 Heavy rainfall on clay soil makes it.........................

Complete the following sentences so that they explain how the following activities of man prevent soil erosion.

51 Growing young trees on the hillside will.........................
52 The sustained yield method of cutting timber will.........................
53 Contour ridging prevents.........................
54 Cover crops of legumes between rubber trees will.........................
55 Terracing involves the.........................

A man finds that the addition of fertiliser to a pond increases the size of fish caught from it two years later.

56 What happens to the fertiliser after it dissolves in the water?
57 How does this affect the size of the fish?
58 Design a carefully controlled experiment to see if the addition to pond water of either nitrate or phosphate promotes better growth of fish.

The 'green revolution' refers to the process of irrigation increasing the availability of land for cultivation.

59 Name three essential features of most irrigation schemes.
60 Name one dangerous disease that is increasing due to the green revolution.

Give the reason for the following processes used in the intensive farming of broiler chickens.

61 caging to reduce movement

62 killing after 3 months rather than 6 months
63 giving accurately weighed amounts of food
64 injection of hormones
65 giving protein-rich diets

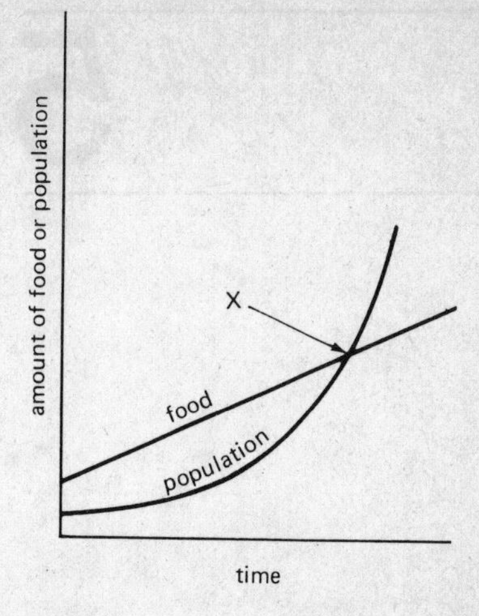

Fig. 9

Examine Fig. 9 and answer the following questions.
66 From the graph, explain the hypothesis put forward by Malthus in 1798.
67 What must happen in the population after the point marked X?
68 Why has the line representing food on this graph not proved correct for most regions in the world?
69 Name three factors which have prevented the population increasing as shown on this graph.
70 What is the name given to the study of human population?

5 The Alimentary Canal

Look at the list of words (A–D) and phrases (1–10) below. Pair off each phrase with the word which you think describes it best. A word may be used more than once.

A amylase
B glucose
C glycerol
D an amino acid

1 a compound formed by the action of trypsin on peptones
2 a basic unit of a polysaccharide
3 a compound de-aminated to carbohydrate
4 a compound converted to glycogen in the liver
5 a compound converted to urea in the liver
6 a compound absorbed by lacteals in the villi
7 a compound made by the action of lipase on its substrate
8 a compound formed by the action of erepsin on dipeptides
9 an active digestive compound in saliva
10 an active digestive compound present in pancreatic juice

11 Teeth missing in the milk dentition are
A incisors.
B canines.
C pre-molars.
D molars.

12 The chemical forming the hard part of bone is called
A calcium phosphate.
B magnesium carbonate.
C calcium carbonate.
D magnesium phosphate.

13 The decay of teeth is started by
A abrasive food substances.
B bacteria producing acids.
C corrosive food substances.
D bacteria feeding on enamel.

14 A disease caused by contaminated food is called
A gingivitis.
B diarrhoea.
C cholera.
D nephritis.

15 Cellulose is useful in the diet because it provides
A carbohydrate.
B crispy food.
C roughage.
D vitamin D.

16 Eating hard crispy food
A stimulates the flow of blood to the teeth.
B provides a supply of vitamin C.
C helps prevent constipation.
D stimulates peristalsis of the intestine.

17 The action of bile on food leaving the stomach is to
A provide fat digesting enzymes.

B r.duce the surface tension of fats.
C acidify the food entering the ileum.
D activate enzymes digesting glycerol.

18 The surface area of the ileum is increased for absorption by
A cilia. C cuboid epithelium.
B brush borders. D striated cells.

19 The large intestine (colon) in man
A absorbs glucose and amino acids.
B stores faeces for elimination.
C absorbs water and salts from faeces.
D contains cellulose digesting bacteria.

20 During their digestion proteins are
A broken down by amylase. C dialysed.
B deaminated. D hydrolysed.

The words in italics include the answers to questions 21–30. Write down the question number with the correct word beside it.
pyloric sphincter, cardiac sphincter, chyme, chyle, symbiosis, absorption, assimilation, carrier, gingivitis, goitre, ascorbic acid, parasite, ptyalin, pepsin, de-amination.

21 an example of an amylase
22 a gum disease
23 a deficiency disease
24 a healthy person with disease bacteria
25 a vitamin
26 liquid leaving the stomach
27 an organism living with another for mutual benefit
28 a structure preventing food entering the duodenum
29 the diffusion of food through the intestinal wall
30 the build-up of protein from amino acids

Examine the diagram of the molar tooth in Fig. 10.
Name the parts numbered **31, 32, 33, 34** and **35.**
36 What is the function of part 34?
37 What structures present in part 32 pass out through the root?
38 Why does food accumulating between teeth cause decay?
39 Why are pregnant mothers likely to suffer from tooth decay?
40 Name the substance which can be added to drinking water to reduce tooth decay.
41 How does this molar tooth differ from an incisor tooth?
42 Why should the toothbrush be used vertically up and down the teeth, rather than horizontally across them?

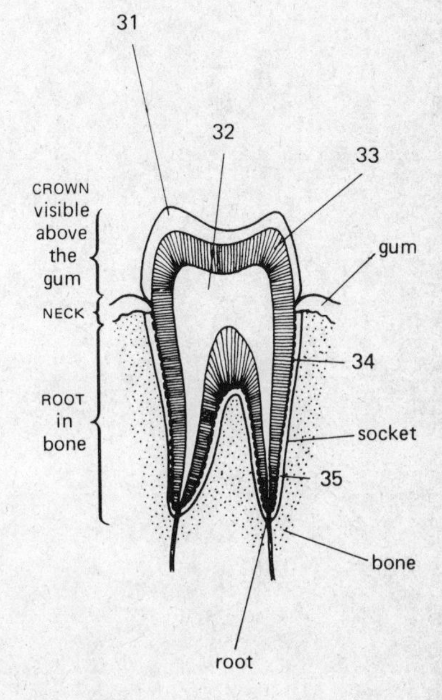

Fig. 10

Examine the diagram Fig. 11 showing an experiment to investigate the effect of saliva on starch and then complete the following table. Beside the number write down the answer which should appear in the table. Also, answer questions 55 to 58.

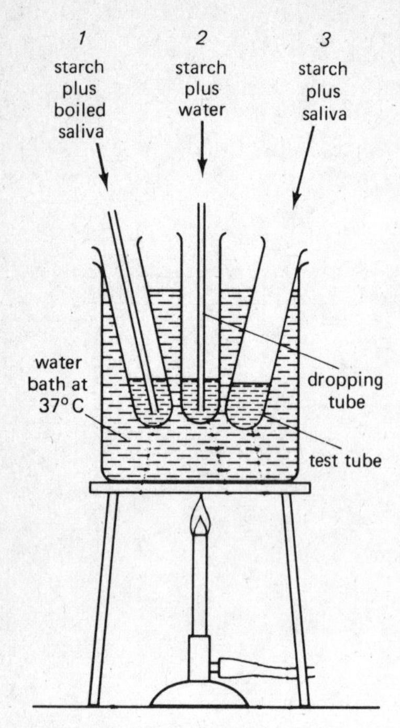

Fig. 11

Tube number	Treatment after 20 minutes	Colour	Reason or conclusion
1	add iodine	**43**	**44**
2	add iodine	**45**	**46**
3	add iodine	**47**	**48**
1	heat with Fehling's	**49**	**50**
2	heat with Fehling's	**51**	**52**
3	heat with Fehling's	**53**	**54**

55 What would be the effect of reducing the temperature in the water bath?
56 What would be the effect of adding hydrochloric acid to tube 3?
57 What would be the effect of boiling the starch with hydrochloric acid?
58 What kind of chemical reaction occurs in this experiment?
59 Name one enzyme (other than ptyalin) which helps break down the starch to reducing sugars, stating where it is produced.
60 What is the function of the stomach muscles?

A drop of pepsin and dilute hydrochloric acid placed on an exposed photographic film made a clear spot in the dark emulsion after 10 minutes.
61 What does this experiment tell us about the nature of the emulsion?
62 What control is necessary to investigate the effect of the hydrochloric acid?
63 Where is pepsin produced in the body?
64 In what main way does an enzyme such as pepsin differ from a chemical catalyst?

Universal indicator is a green colour when neutral but turns yellow below pH7 and blue above pH7. Some indicator was added to tube A containing milk, lipase and bile salts, tube B, containing milk and lipase and tube C which contains milk and bile.
65 What colour would the indicator show initially in tube A?
66 What is responsible for this colour in tube A?
67 In which tube will the colour change first and what colour will form?
68 What would be responsible for the colour change?
69 What two effects has the bile in these experiments?
70 Where is bile produced in the body?
71 Where is the lipase produced in the body?

Give a reason for the colour this indicator would appear in each of the following.

72 the stomach

73 the duodenum

74 sour milk

Name the parts of the alimentary canal numbered **75, 76, 77, 78, 79, 80, 81, 82, 83, 84** in Fig. 12.

Name or give the number of the part of the alimentary canal associated with

85 hookworm.

86 peptic ulcer.

87 diabetes.

88 amoebic dysentery.

89 What may happen if food such as pips block the appendix?

90 What is the function of part 77?

91 What is the function of part 81?

92 What is the name given to the muscular movements which move food in the gut?

93 Name a part labelled on this diagram which is not part of the digestive system.

94 Name a juice containing digestive enzymes which pours onto food at the part labelled 78.

95 Name two enzymes secreted by the ileum and explain their action.

Fill in the gaps to complete the following sentences.
The end products of protein digestion are **96** and the end product of carbohydrate digestion is **97** which are absorbed into **98** in the villi. From here they pass along the **99** vein to the liver.

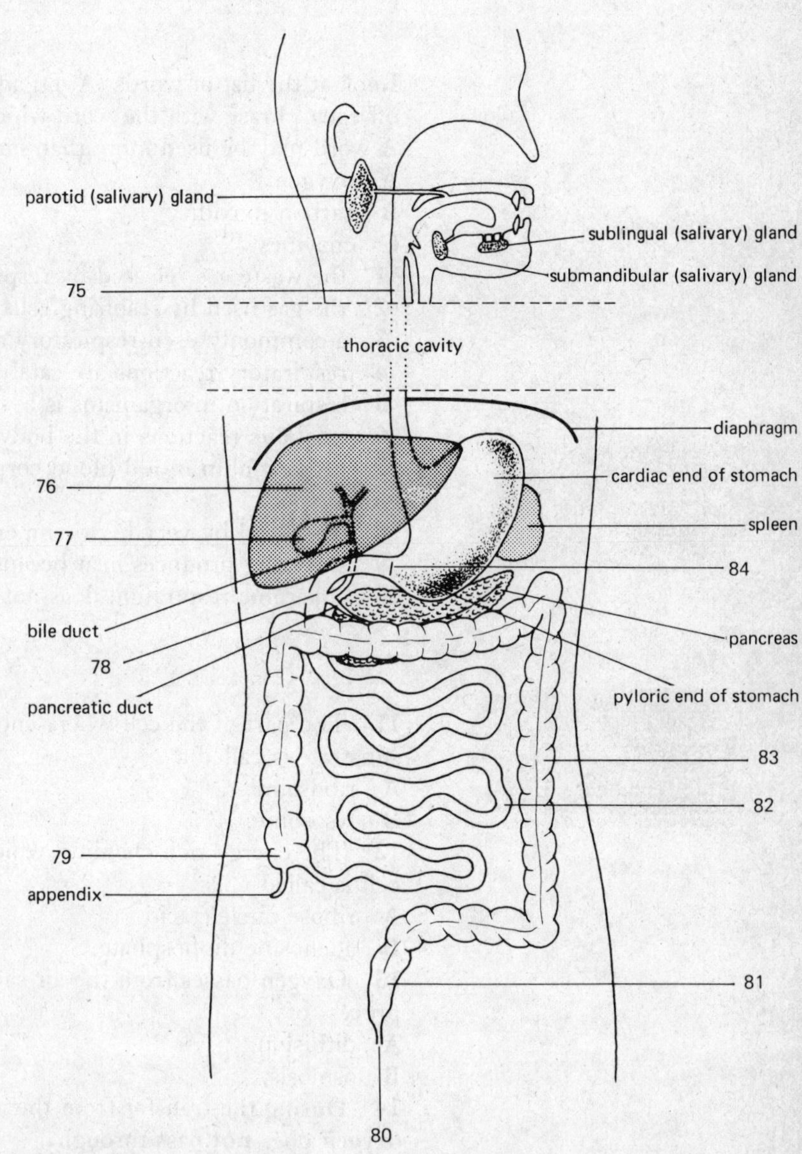

Fig. 12

6 Respiration

Look at the list of words (A–D) and phrases (1–10) below. Pair off each phrase with the word which you think describes it best. A word may be used more than once.

A oxygen.
B carbon dioxide
C enzymes
D heat
E glucose

1 the waste gas released by respiring cells
2 the gas used by respiring cells
3 a commonly used respiratory substrate
4 respiratory reactions are catalysed by
5 respiration in organisms is best detected by its release
6 catabolic reactions in the body involve its release
7 haemoglobin in red blood corpuscles is mainly important for its transport
8 destroyed by very high temperatures
9 shivering produces heat because of its breakdown
10 anaerobic respiration does not involve its intake

11 The part of the cell where energy is released from the food substrate is called a
A ribosome.
B lysosome.
C Golgi body.
D mitochondrion.

12 The energy rich chemical which stores energy for use in the cell is called
A ribose nucleic acid.
B adenosine diphosphate.
C deoxyribose nucleic acid.
D adenosine triphosphate.

13 Oxygen passes from the air sacs to the blood capillaries by the process of
A diffusion.
B osmosis.
C air sac contraction.
D diaphragm contraction.

14 During the transfer from the alveolus to the haemoglobin oxygen does **not** pass through
A alveolar membranes.
B blood plasma.
C arteriole walls.
D erythrocyte membranes.

Write down the number of the gap with the word beside it which best fills the gap to complete the sentences.

Anaerobic respiration occurs in the cells of **15** and the

products of this process are **16** and **17**. This process, important in the making of wine, is also called **18**. The enzymes responsible are known as the **19** complex, and they act on **20** substrates from grapes.

Write down the names of the parts numbered **21 to 27** on the diagram Fig. 13 opposite. Briefly explain the main function of the parts numbered **28, 29, 30,** and **31.**
32 In their correct order starting from the nose, list five main parts of the respiratory system through which air will pass to reach the air sacs.
33 What is the effect of shallow breathing on the part numbered 33?
34 What signs would you expect on part numbered 26 if the person suffered from tuberculosis?
35 How do medical personnel discover these signs on part 26?
36 What causes these signs?
37 Give one other early sign indicating tuberculosis.
38 Name two other common diseases of the respiratory system.
39 Why does adequate room ventilation help prevent respiratory disease?

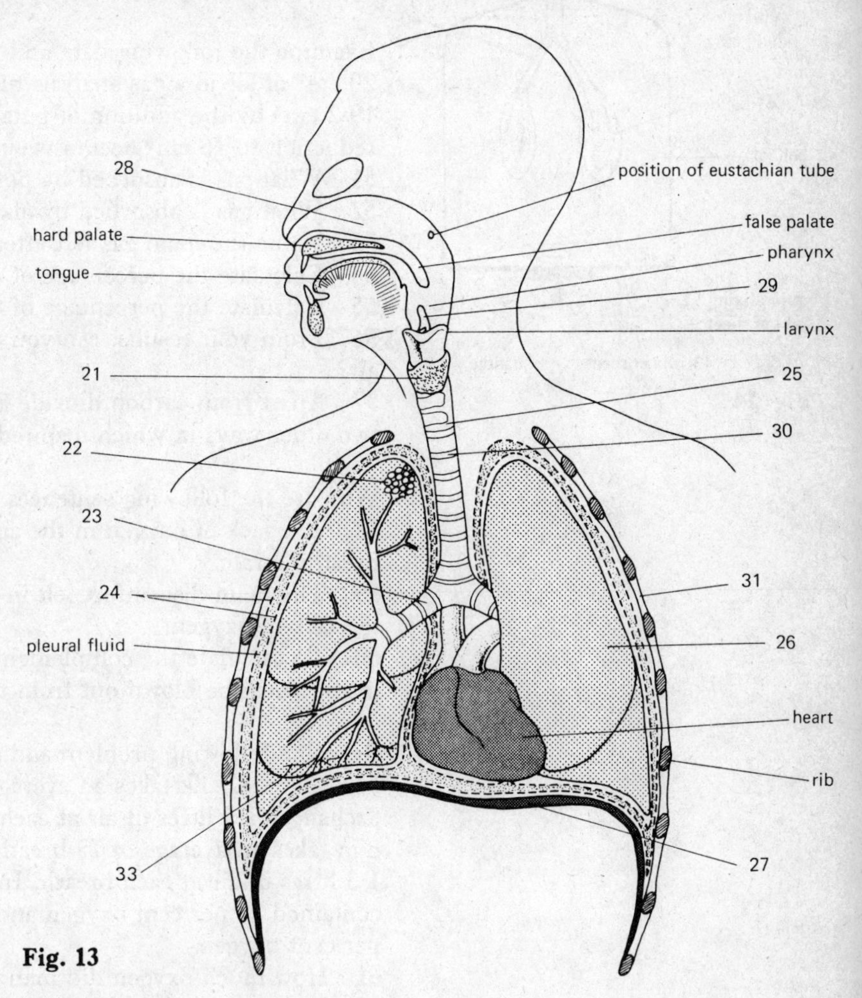

Fig. 13

The diagram in Fig. 14 shows a model to illustrate some of the movements involved in breathing. The vertical section of the Y tube represents the trachea. What do the parts numbered **40, 41, 42** and **43** represent?
44 What is the effect on part 41 of pulling the handle down?
45 What happens to the air in the bell jar when the handle is pulled down?
46 What process does this illustrate in breathing?
47 What happens to the external intercostal muscles during this process?
48 Which part of the thorax moves during breathing, but does not move on this model?

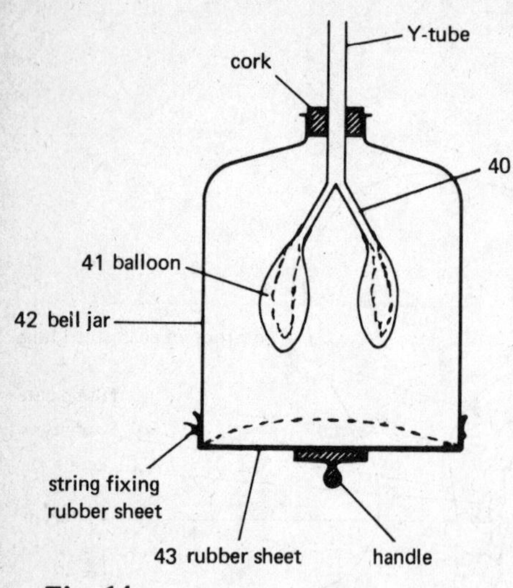

Fig. 14

49 Which muscles are frequently damaged in poliomyelitis, so stopping breathing?
50 Name the machine which enables patients to survive after an attack of poliomyelitis which affects the lungs.

Examine the following data and answer questions 51 to 57.
20 cm^3 of air in a gas analysis tube is reduced in volume to 19·2 cm^3 by the addition of potassium hydroxide. A further reduction to 16 cm^3 occurs when alkaline pyrogallol is introduced.
51 What gas is absorbed by potassium hydroxide?
52 What gas is absorbed by alkaline pyrogallol?
53 Name the main gas left after this absorption.
54 Calculate the percentage of carbon dioxide in this air sample
55 Calculate the percentage of oxygen in this air sample.
56 From your results, can you tell if this is inspired or expired air?
57 Apart from carbon dioxide and oxygen content, write down two other ways in which inspired air differs from expired air.

Why are the following sentences incorrect?
58 The lack of oxygen in the air causes an increase in the breathing rate.
59 The main discomfort felt in badly ventilated rooms is due to the lack of oxygen.
60 To calculate the complemental air using an instrument, all the air must be blown out from the lungs.

Read the following problem and answer questions 61 to 66.
Man X on a walk takes an average of 16 breaths per minute and exchanges 1·5 litres of air at each breath. Man Y walking beside him takes an average of 15 breaths per minute and exchanges 1·3 litres of air at each breath. In both cases the inspired air contained 20 per cent oxygen and the expired air contained 16 per cent oxygen.
61 How much oxygen did man X use per minute?
62 How much oxygen did man Y use per minute?
63 Make two hypotheses to account for the difference in oxygen consumption between man X and man Y assuming they walked at exactly the same speed and for the same distance.
64 What two effects on breathing would occur if they ran?
65 In what way would you expect these figures to differ if the men were at a high altitude?
66 What accounts for these differences at high altitudes?
67 In what way does cigarette smoking initially affect the lung tissue?
68 In what ways have statistics shown that smoking affects the lungs over a long period of time?
69 What is the reason for the typical 'smoker's cough'?

Ex· nine the graph in Fig. 15, and answer questions 70 to 74.

70 What instrument is used to give you the figures to produce this graph?

How would this instrument mark on this graph

71 complemental air?

72 supplemental air?

73 How would the graph vary after taking exercise?

74 A typical figure for the vital capacity of a man would be

A 2 litres. C 5 litres.

B 3½ litres. D 10 litres.

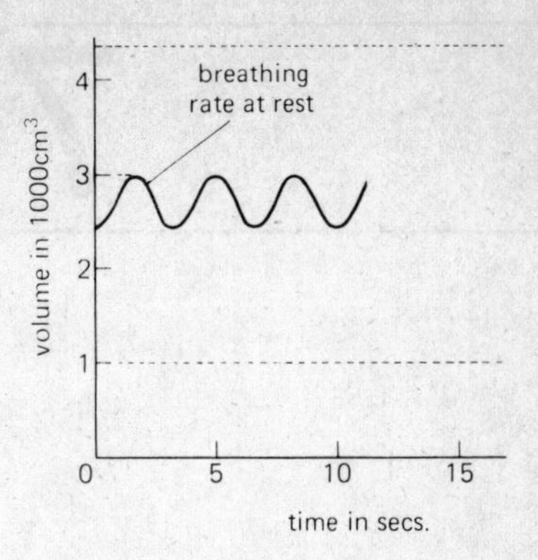

Fig. 15

75 Using the apparatus below, in Fig. 16, design an experiment to show the intake of oxygen by an insect. You are also given potassium hydroxide pellets, an insect and another set of this apparatus.

76 Indicate two likely experimental errors in the experiment described for question 75.

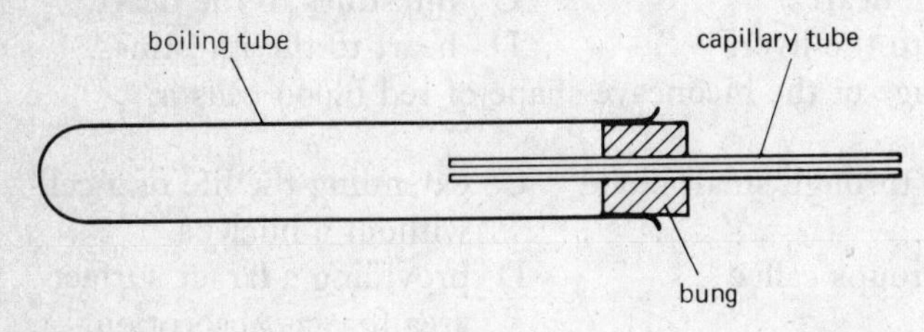

Fig. 16

7 Circulatory system

1 The chamber of the heart with the most muscular wall is called the

A left ventricle.
B left auricle.
C right ventricle.
D right auricle.

2 The pulmonary artery carries blood which is

A oxygenated to the heart.
B de-oxygenated from the heart.
C oxygenated from the heart.
D de-oxygenated to the heart.

3 The hepatic portal vein carries blood from the

A liver to the heart.
B intestines to the liver.
C intestines to the heart.
D heart to the intestines.

4 An advantage of the biconcave shape of red blood cells is for

A squeezing through small blood capillaries.
B forming groups called rouleaux.
C extending the life of a cell without a nucleus.
D providing a larger surface area for gas absorption.

5 The number of red blood cells in 1 cm^3 of blood is approximately

A 50 000.
B 500 000.
C 5 000 000.
D 5 000 000 000.

6 Carbon dioxide is mainly transported

A in erythrocytes.
B in leucocytes.
C as bicarbonates in the plasma.
D as dissolved gas in the plasma.

7 Blood is prevented from clotting by

A sodium citrate.
B calcium chloride.
C fibrinogen.
D thrombokinase.

8 A disease in which blood fails to clot is called

A haemolysis.
B haemopoiesis.
C haematuria.
D haemophilia.

9 The type of immunity gained by a person recovering from a bacterial disease is called

A innate.
B natural active acquired.
C artificial active acquired.
D artificial passive acquired.

10 The best treatment following a snake bite is to inject

A anti-snake venom serum.
B snake venom antigens.
C snake venom vaccine.
D attenuated snake venom.

The following statements are either always true (T), always false (F), or only true sometimes (S). Write beside the number of the question, the capital letter T, F or S accordingly.

11 Mature human red blood cells lack a nucleus.
12 Arteries carry blood away from the heart.
13 Arteries carry oxygenated blood.
14 A person of blood group A can receive a transfusion of blood group AB, provided it is matched in all other respects.
15 The pulse rate in adults is 72 per minute.
16 Lymph passes in one direction along lymph vessels.
17 Plasma cells can produce antibodies.
18 Sickle cell anaemia is a disease of the leucocytes.
19 If a rhesus negative mother has a rhesus positive child, then rhesus positive antibodies are induced in her blood.
20 The nutrients for the heart are extracted from the blood while flowing through its chambers.

Match the following pairs by writing down the number of the word or words from column X with the letter of the definition in column Y which best agrees with it.

	X		Y
21	lymph	A	released by platelets at a wound
22	tissue fluid	B	the fluid part of normal blood
23	plasma	C	the scientist who discovered that blood circulates in the body
24	serum	D	the scientist who developed a vaccine for rabies
25	Pasteur	E	the fluid immediately bathing cells
26	Jenner	F	the fluid draining away from cells
27	Harvey	G	the fluid (minus fibrinogen) separating from clotted blood
28	thrombokinase	H	relaxation of auricles and ventricles
29	systole	I	the scientist who provided immunity to smallpox
30	diastole	J	muscular contraction of auricles and ventricles

Examine the diagram of the heart in Fig. 17 and write down the names of the parts labelled **31, 32, 33, 34, 35, 36, 37, 38, 39** and **40.**

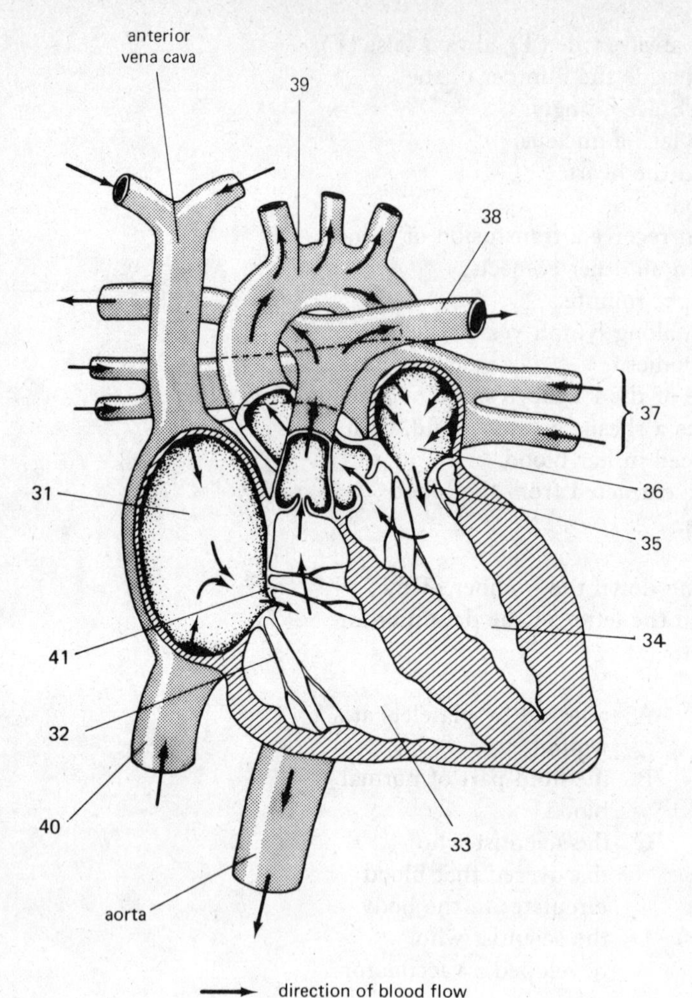

Fig. 17

41 What is the function of part 41?
42 What is the function of part 32?
43 What is the function of part 38?
44 What kind of blood is found in part 33?
45 What is the purpose of the muscles associated with part 34?
46 What is the name of the heart muscle?
47 What is the special physiological feature of this heart muscle?
48 Which numbered guideline points nearest to the pacemaker controlling the heart beat?
49 Which vessel not shown on the diagram becomes blocked thus causing coronary thrombosis?
50 What is the effect on blood pressure of atrophy of the heart muscle?
51 In some rare cases babies have a hole in the septum between parts 33 and 34. What would you observe about such babies and what is the cause of the features observed?

Examine the diagram of the circulatory system in Fig. 18 and write down the names of the parts labelled **52, 53, 54, 55** and **56.**
57 Write down in the correct order the names of the blood vessels and organs through which blood would pass to travel from the intestines to the legs.
58 Where is blood passing from in part 58?
59 Name three ways in which the wall of the subclavian vein differs from the wall of the subclavian artery.
60 What three factors assist the flow of blood in the right femoral vein?
61 What is the effect on the blood pressure of the deposition of fat in the arteries?
62 Write down three main ways in which you would expect the blood to differ in composition in the hepatic portal vein, from that in the mesenteric artery.

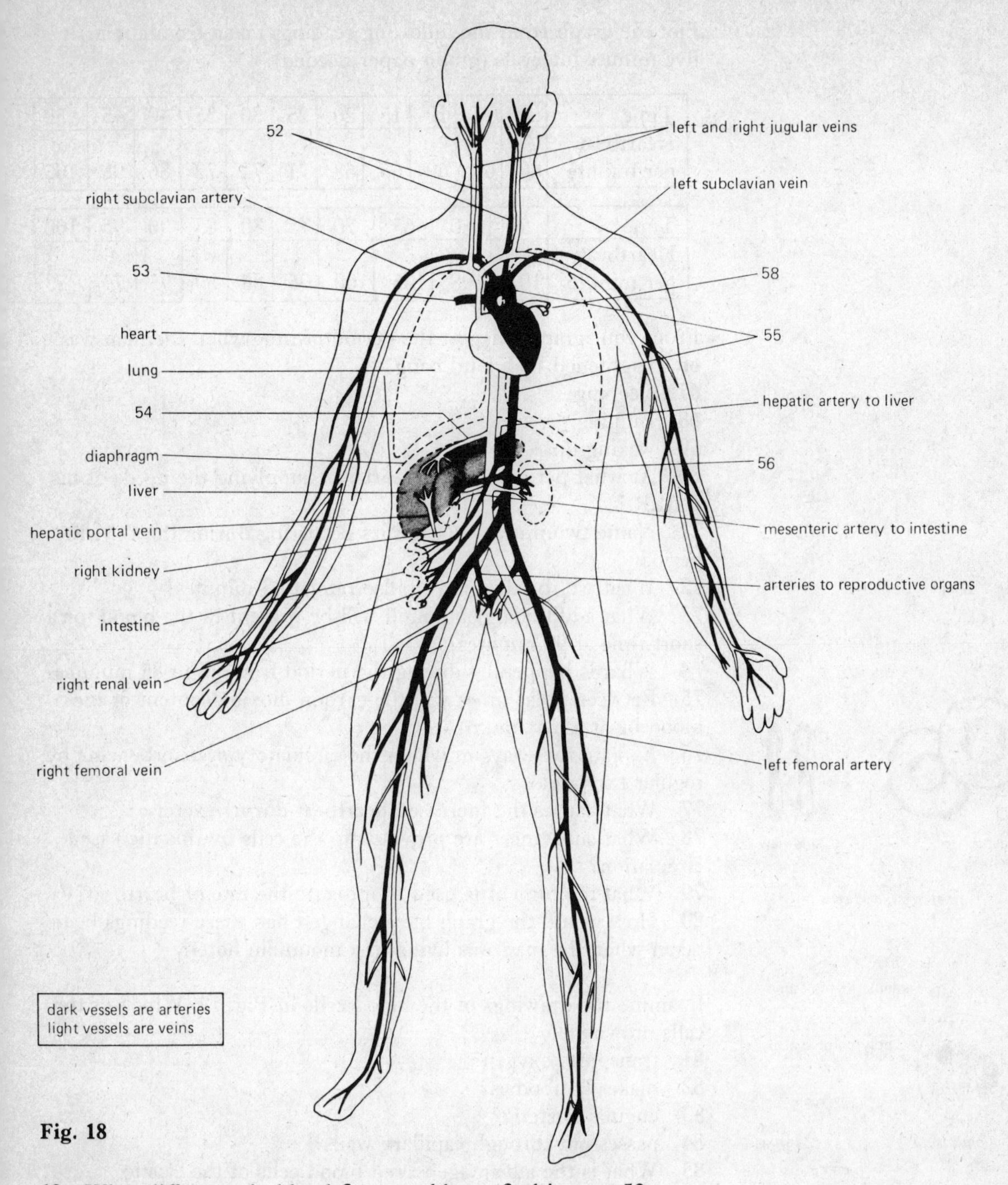

Fig. 18

63 What difference in blood flow would you find in part 52 when compared with part 54?

64 Name the important main vein not labelled with a guideline on this diagram.

65 In which vessel shown on this diagram would a lack of oxygen quickly induce fainting?

Plot the graph from the following readings taken from a man at five minute intervals (graph paper needed).

Time	0	5	10	15	20	25	30	35	40	45	50
Heartbeat per minute	60	60	60	65	68	71	72	72	86	98	105

Time	55	60	65	70	75	80	85	90	95	100
Heartbeat per minute	107	108	105	100	95	88	80	95	74	73

From your graph, suggest the period of time when the man was

66 frightened by a loud bang.
67 sleeping.
68 running.
69 waking up.
70 At what period was the heart just supplying the needs of his B.M.R.?
71 Name two muscular activities occurring during the B.M.R. period.
72 What will be the man's pulse rate at 43 minutes?
73 What additional compound will be present in the blood for a short time at 90 minutes?
74 What is happening during the period from 65 to 85 minutes?
75 Between what times will the carbon dioxide content of the blood be at a maximum?
76 Explain two ways in which the circulatory system benefits by regular exercise.
77 What causes the increased heartbeat during exercise?
78 What substances are provided to the cells by this increased circulation?
79 What instrument is used to measure the rate of heartbeat?
80 How would the graph have changed had these readings been taken when the man was living in a mountain hotel?

Fig. 19

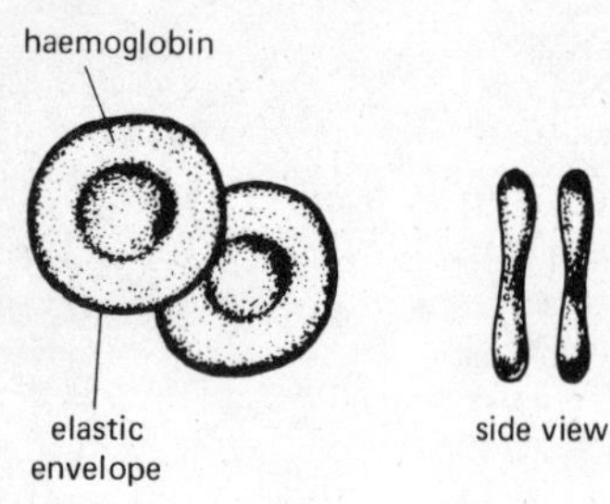

a) red blood cells

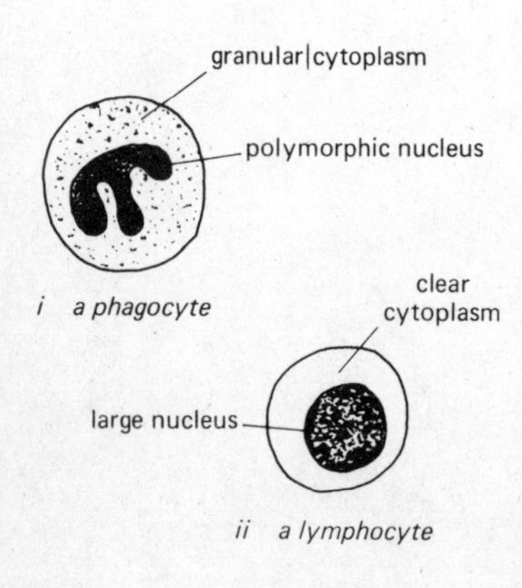

b) white blood cell

Examine the drawings of the blood cells in Fig. 19. Which of the cells drawn

81 transports oxygen?
82 makes antibodies?
83 engulfs bacteria?
84 passes out through capillary walls?
85 What is the advantage to red blood cells of the elastic envelope?
86 Name the condition which is caused by a lack of red blood cells.
87 Which compound in these cells requires iron in the diet for its formation?
88 Name four substances transported by blood plasma.

The Skeleton

8

Examine in Fig. 20 the diagram of the skeleton, eight functions of which are listed below. For each function, select an example of a part of the skeleton which performs that function and explain in one sentence how the function is performed. (Question 1 has been done for you as an example.)

1 support (answer: Vertebrae support the skull.)
2 protection
3 muscle attachment
4 acts as a lever
5 allows movement
6 makes red cells
7 provides shape
8 calcium reserve
9 Name any two parts on this diagram where cartilage is found.
10 For the parts named in question 9, explain the importance of the flexibility of the cartilage in that region.
Name the parts on the diagram Fig. 20 labelled **11, 12, 13, 14, 15, 16, 17, 18, 19** and **20.**
21 How does the structure at point X differ in a baby from the same structure in an adult.
22 Where would you find a fixed joint on the skeleton?

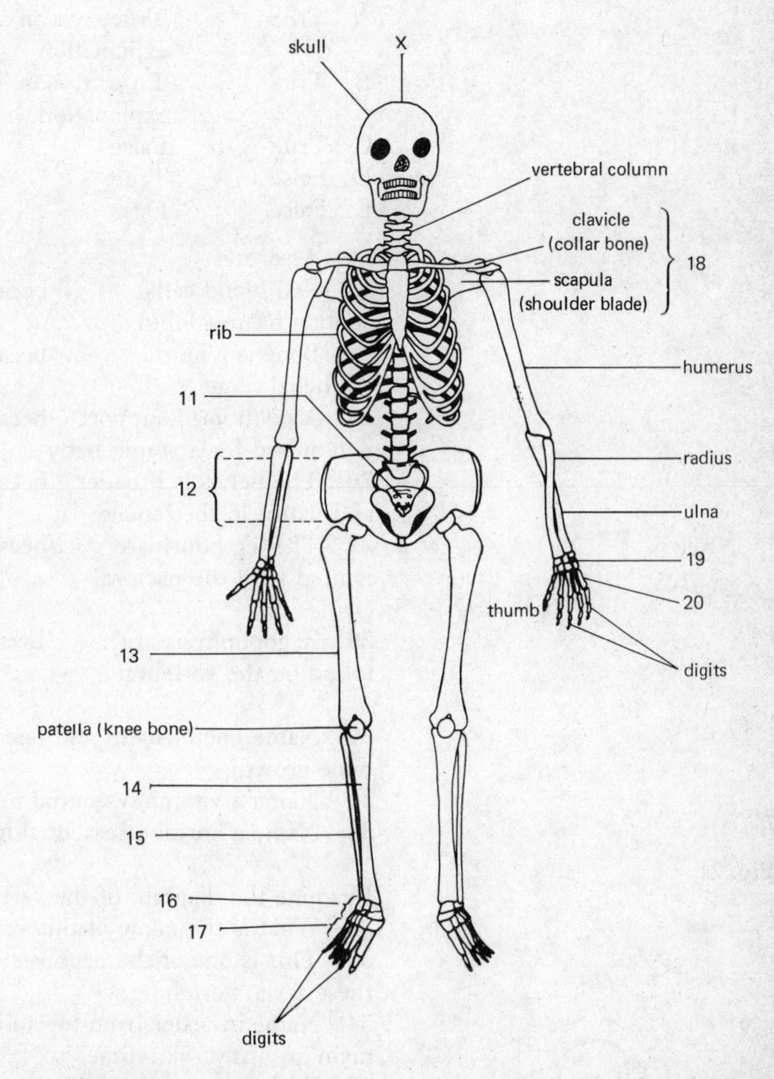

Fig. 20

The following statements (23–28) are made up of an assertion followed by a reason. Write down alongside the question number
A if both assertion and reason are true statements and the reason is a correct explanation of the assertion

B if both assertion and reason are true statements, but the reason is not a correct explanation of the assertion
C if the assertion is true, but the reason is a false statement
D if the assertion is false, but the reason is a true statement
E if both assertion and reason are false statements.
This can be summarized:

	Assertion	Reason
A	True	True: reason is correct explanation
B	True	True: reason is not a correct explanation.
C	True	False
D	False	True
E	False	False

Assertion		Reason
23 Red blood cells contain haemoglobin	because	red blood cells are made in the red bone marrow.
24 Bone is a hard epithelial tissue	because	bone matrix is impregnated with calcium salts.
25 A good head support is required for a young baby	because	baby's neck muscles cannot support the head.
26 The pelvis is broader and flatter in the female	because	the baby has to pass through the pelvis at childbirth.
27 The leg bones are jointed with the pectoral girdle	because	there is a ball and socket joint at the pectoral girdle.
28 Zygopophysis are found on the vertebrae	because	zygopophysis surround and protect the spinal cord.

29 Name one element and one salt essential in the diet for healthy bone growth.
30 Name a vitamin essential in the diet for healthy bone growth.
31 Name a hormone essential in the body for healthy bone growth.

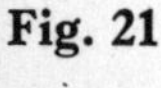
Fig. 21

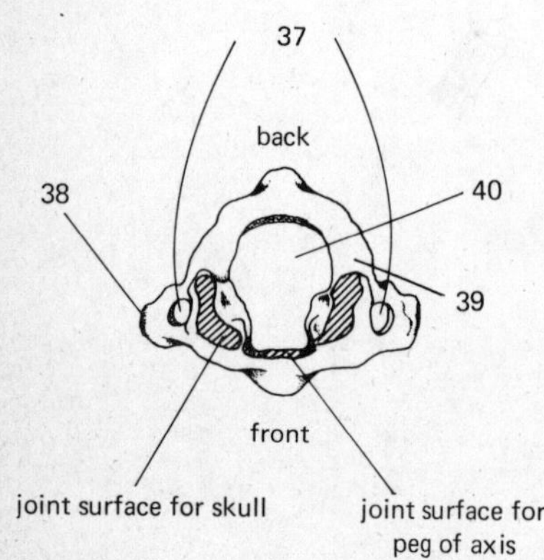

Examine the diagram of the vertebra in Fig. 21.
32 What is the name of this vertebra?
33 This is one of the neck vertebrae. What is the name given to these seven vertebrae?
34 Name in order from top to bottom of the spine the other main groups of vertebrae.
35 Explain for each of these main groups of vertebrae, one way in which they differ in structure and one way in which they differ in function from the vertebra drawn.
36 What part present in all other vertebrae is missing from the vertebra in Fig. 21?
Name the parts **37, 38, 39** and **40** on the diagram in Fig. 21.
41 In which direction does the skull move on this vertebra?

42 In which direction does this vertebra move on the axis?
43 What structure passes through part 40?
44 What structure passes through part 37?
45 What structure separates one vertebra from another and what is the function of this structure?

Examine the synovial joint in Fig. 22 and answer questions **46** to **55**
Name the parts numbered **46, 47, 48** and **49.**
50 What kind of joint is drawn?
51 What kind of movement does this joint allow?
52 Name two structures which reduce friction at this joint.
53 Which structures support the joint but are elastic to allow movement?
54 Name the disease affecting joints.
55 Which part of a joint is most likely to become damaged when it is dislocated as a result of a fall?

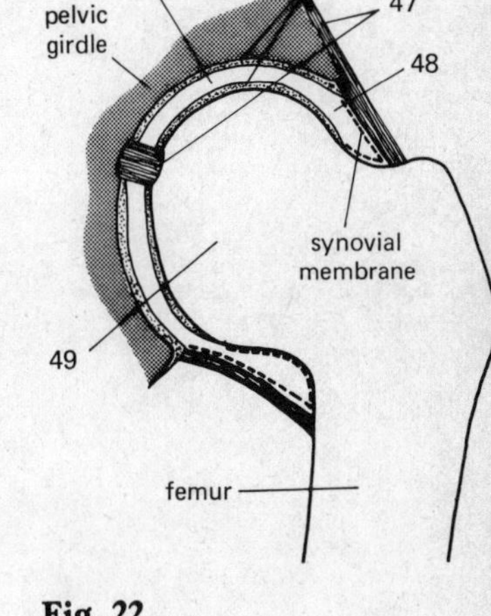

Fig. 22

From the answers listed in italics at the end of these questions, select an example of
56 a bad form of posture affecting the abdominal muscles.
57 the basic structure of vertebrate limbs.
58 the membrane covering bone to which tendons are attached.
59 the non-elastic fibres in tendons.
60 the cavity into which the head of the femur fits.
61 a condition describing the tension in healthy muscle.
62 the protein ground substance in the matrix of cartilage.
63 the point of support for a lever such as occurs at joints.
64 a bad form of posture affecting breathing movements.
65 the tendon fixed to the movable bone at a joint.
pentadactyl collagen periosteum
chondrin glenoid acetabulum
fulcrum insertion
origin hollow back
round shoulder tone

Examine the diagram of the arm in Fig. 23 and write down the names of the parts labelled **66, 67, 68, 69, 70, 71** and **72.** Complete the following sentences by writing down the most appropriate word in each case. You will need to refer to Fig. 23 for some of your answers.

Fig. 23

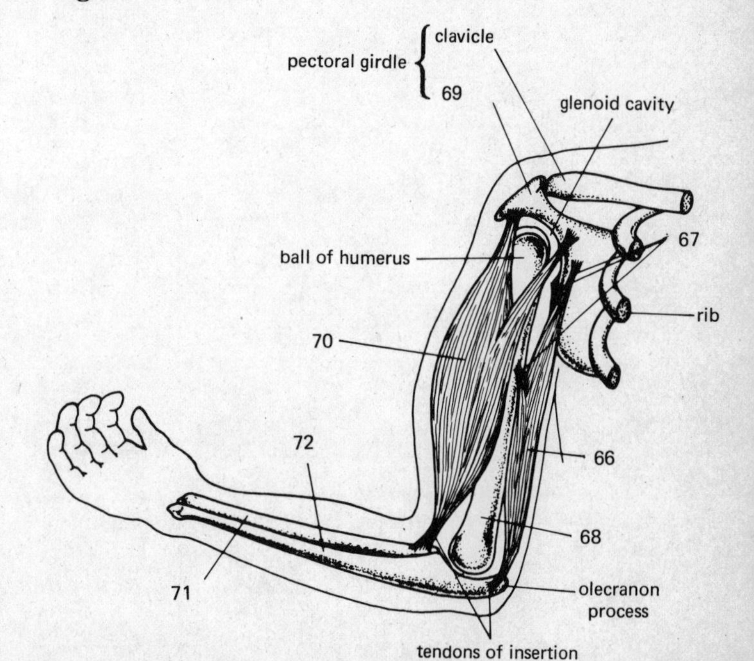

When the arm bends (flexes) at the elbow, the triceps muscle will **73** , while the biceps muscle will **74** . This double action of muscle is described as being **75** . The bone in the upper arm acts as a **76** on the two bones in the lower arm. Movement at the elbow occurs in one plane only because of a **77** joint although the hand can be twisted as the two bones form a **78** joint at the elbow. At the shoulder is a **79** joint which allows almost complete rotation. Muscle contraction is initiated by the brain which sends a **80** to the muscle which is described as **81** because it is under conscious control. A high energy compound in the muscle called **82** loses phosphate to form **83** during muscle activity.

84 A man holds a 50 g weight in his hand which is 40 cm from the fulcrum at his elbow joint. If his biceps is attached to the bone at 2 cm from the fulcrum, what effort must his biceps apply to support this weight? (Ignore the weight of his arm.)

85 What order of lever has been considered in question 84?

Excretion and the Skin 9

Examine the following table which shows the main waste products of the body and the main organs from which they are excreted.

	Excretory organ			
Waste product	Skin	Kidney	Lung	Alimentary canal
Urea	**1**	**2**	**3**	**4**
Salts	**5**	**6**	**7**	**8**
Carbon dioxide	**9**	**10**	**11**	**12**
Bile	**13**	**14**	**15**	**16**
Water	**17**	**18**	**19**	**20**

Beside the numbers taken from the table above, write down
N if the organ does **not** excrete the waste product.
T if the organ excretes a **trace** of the waste product.
S if the organ excretes a **significant** amount of the waste product.

Match the following pairs by writing down the number of the word in column X with the letter of the correct definition in column Y.

	X		Y
21	homeostasis	A	passage of urine by relaxation of a sphincter muscle in the bladder
22	plasmolysed	B	enzyme converting glycogen to glucose
23	osmosis	C	cells lacking support due to loss of water
24	dialysis	D	self regulating processes maintaining constant conditions
25	diffusion	E	passage of water through a semi-permeable membrane from a weaker to a more concentrated solution
26	micturition	F	cells rigid due to inflation with water.
27	turgidity	G	passage of molecules from a greater to a lesser concentration

28 glycogenase — H hormone converting glucose to glycogen

29 insulin — I elimination of undigested food

30 egestion — J passage of true solutions through a membrane which prevents the passage of a colloid.

31 At 100 per cent relative humidity, a wet and dry bulb hygrometer will show the dry bulb reading.

A 100 per cent above the wet bulb
B equal to that of the wet bulb.
C lower than the wet bulb.
D greater than the wet bulb.

32 The action of sunlight on ergosterol in the skin is to synthesise

A vitamin D.
B vitamin A.
C vitamin B_1.
D vitamin C.

33 The control of the body temperature is assisted by

A diffusion.
B osmosis.
C evaporation.
D dialysis.

34 Clean and dry skin is essential to prevent parasitism by organisms causing

A *Tinea*
B *Taenia*
C thrush.
D typhus.

35 The filtrate within the Bowman's capsule contains most of the blood's

A albumins.
B globulins.
C plasma.
D erythrocytes.

36 Sebum is **not** important in the skin to

A keep out water.
B destroy micro-organisms.
C evaporate sweat.
D have supple epidermal cells.

37 Erector muscles in the skin do **not**

A contract during sweating.
B contract during shivering.
C cause a tingling feeling after fright.
D erect the fur on a cat's body.

38 Loss of heat from the body is increased by

A vaso-dilation.
B sub-cutaneous fat.
C blood reservoir in the liver
D clothing.

39 · Fluid passes from the blood to the Bowman's capsule by

A osmotic pressure.
C ultra-filtration.

B diffusion.

D the smaller diameter of the afferent than the efferent arteriole.

40 The body temperature is raised by
A expiration of air.
B vaso-dilation of capillaries.
C metabolism of food.
D radiation of heat.

Each of the following statements is incorrect in one respect. By adding, deleting or changing words re-write each sentence correctly.

41 Sweating cools the body.
42 Undigested food is excreted from the body in faeces.
43 Traces of urea are secreted from the body in sweat.
44 Cells in distilled water become plasmolysed.
45 The liver stores protein and glycogen.

Examine in Fig. 24 the diagram of the skin and name the parts labelled **46, 47, 48, 49, 50, 51, 52, 53, 54** and **55.**

56 What is the function of part 55?
57 What is the function of the secretion from part 54?
58 What will be the effect of an increased body temperature on part 53?
59 What will be the effect of an increased body temperature on the blood capillaries?
60 Where would you find melanin in the skin?
61 What is the function of melanin?
62 Loss of tension occurs with age in the connective tissue of the skin. What observable effect has this on the skin?
63 In what **two** ways does the part labelled 52 help control the body temperature?

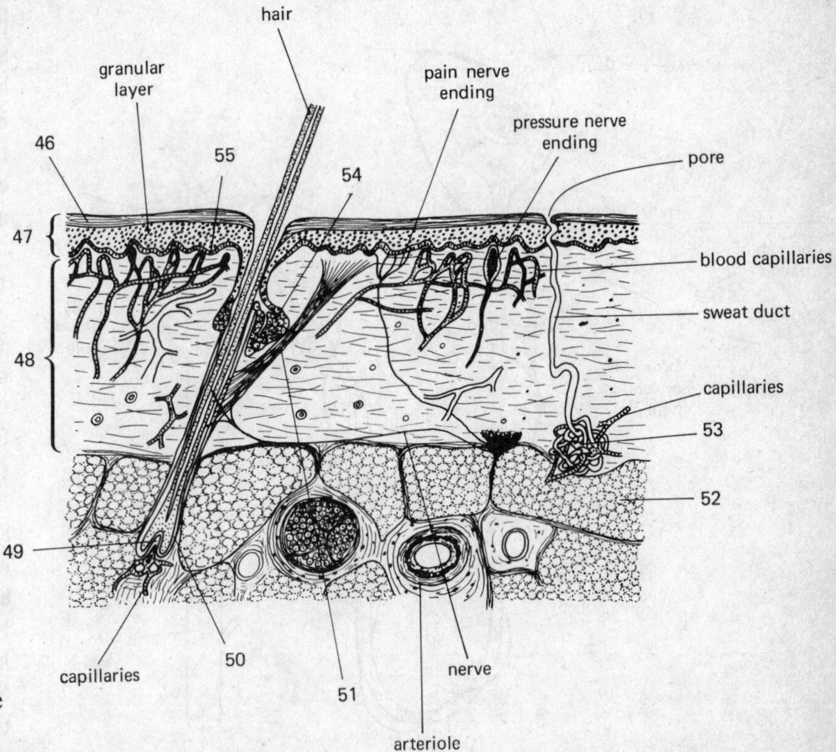

Fig. 24 From *Introduction to Biology* by D. G. Mackean, John Murray Ltd.

64 Why does a fan help to reduce the body temperature?
65 What causes heat exhaustion?
66 Explain two ways in which the diet should be varied when excessive sweating occurs.
67 In what regions of the body is part 46 particularly thick?
68 Why is the skin thick in these regions?

What kind of organism found in the skin is responsible for the disease of

69 athlete's foot?

70 scabies?

For each of the following types of clothing, state one feature of their structure and the importance of this feature in a particular climate.

Clothing	Structure	Importance
wool	**71**	**72**
cotton	**73**	**74**
nylon	**75**	**76**

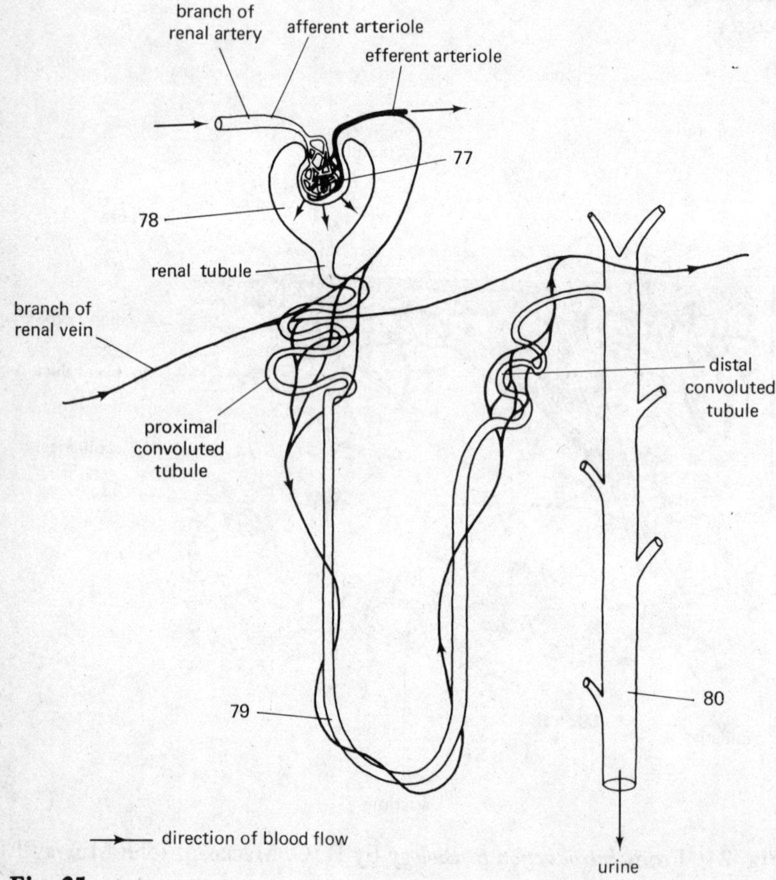

Fig. 25

Examine the diagram of a renal tubule in Fig. 25 and name the parts labelled **77, 78, 79** and **80.**

81 In what region of the kidney is part 78 found?

82 State two differences between the blood in the efferent arteriole and the afferent arteriole.

Read the following sentence and answer questions 83 and 84. The filtrate in part 78 contains more water and salts than the urine at part 80.

83 How and in which parts is this concentration mainly changed?

84 Name the three main components of urine.

85 By what process is the blood purified in an artificial kidney machine?

86 Name in the correct order the parts of the body through which the urine passes in travelling from part 80 to the exterior.

Read the following problem and answer questions 87 and 88. A tissue placed in a salt solution A loses weight, but gains weight when it is transferred to a salt solution B. What is the difference

87 between solutions A and B?

88 between solution A and the cell contents?

89 What process causes these weight differences?
90 If the tissue was killed in chloroform vapour, what weight difference would occur in solution B? Explain your answer.

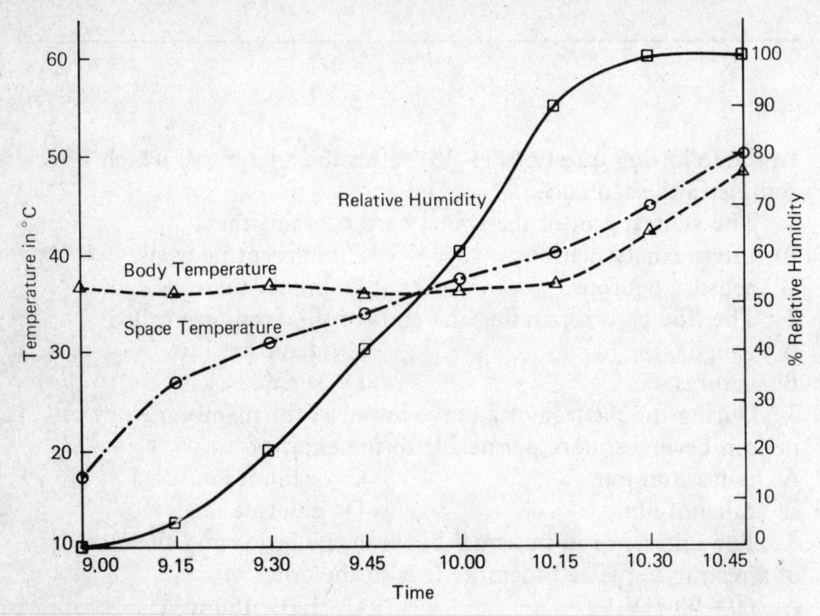

Fig. 26

The graph in Fig. 26 shows the body temperature of a naked man enclosed in a confined space. In addition the temperature and relative humidity of the air in this space from 9 am until 10.45 am is also recorded. Use this data to help answer questions 91 to 103.
What kind of instrument is used to measure
91 the body temperature of the man?
92 the relative humidity of the space?

At what time will the two readings on the instrument detecting the relative humidity be
93 the most different?
94 the same?
95 What is the temperature of the space at 9.30 am in °C?
During which period
96 are the skin capillaries likely to be constricted?
97 will sweating take place?
98 will the sweat not evaporate?
99 is heat exhaustion likely?
100 What are the symptoms of heat exhaustion?
101 How would you treat the man for heat exhaustion?
102 Which condition in the confined space is best changed in order to prevent this heat exhaustion occuring?
103 What body processes will be helping to control the body temperature between 9 am and 9.15 am?

10 The Nervous System

In the following questions (1–15) select the alternative which best completes the sentence.

1 The ventral root of the spinal cord contains the
A intermediate neurons. C afferent neurons.
B sensory neurons. D motor neurons.

2 The tiny gaps separating the ends of the axons are called
A ganglia. C dendrites.
B sutures. D synapses.

3 During the passage of a nerve impulse, the membrane of the neuron becomes more permeable to the entry of
A potassium ion. C sodium ion.
B calcium ion. D chloride ion.

4 The difference in potential between the inside and the outside of a resting nerve cell membrane is in the order of
A 60 – 90 mV. C 120 – 150 mV.
B 90 – 120 mV. D 150 – 180 mV.

5 Blinking the eyes to avoid the danger from an initially un-noticed flying insect is an example of a
A spinal reflex. C endocrine action.
B voluntary action. D cranial reflex.

6 Walking is an example of a
A sympathetic reflex. C cranial reflex.
B conditioned reflex. D inborn reflex.

7 The spinal cord enlarges as it first enters the brain to form the
A cerebrum. C medulla oblongata.
B foramen magnum. D cerebellum.

8 The autonomic nervous system has **no** influence over the control of
A cardiac muscle contraction.
B diaphragm muscle contraction.
C gastrocnemius muscle contraction.
D sweat secretion.

9 Receptors are found in the skin detecting
A light. C humidity.
B gravity. D temperature.

10 Effectors found in the skin include
A bulbous corpuscles. C malpighian cells.
B erector muscles. D hair follicles.

11 Most of the refraction of light in the eye occurs in the
A cornea. C aqueous humour.

B vitreous humour. D lens.

12 The condition when near objects cannot be focused because the diverging rays of light cannot be sufficiently refracted is called
A long sight (hypermetropia). C old sight (presbyopia).
B short sight (myopia). D astigmatism.

13 Underactivity of the thyroid gland reduces the secretion of thyroxine which
A increases growth. C reduces growth.
B increases mental development. D causes overactivity.

14 The hormone insulin is secreted by
A liver cells. C adrenal glands.
B islets of Langerhans. D pituitary glands.

15 The function of the eustachian tube is to equalise pressure between
A the middle and inner ear. C the inner ear and pharynx.
B the middle ear and pharnyx. D the outer ear and inner ear.

The diagram in Fig. 27 represents a section of the spinal cord in the region of the shoulders.

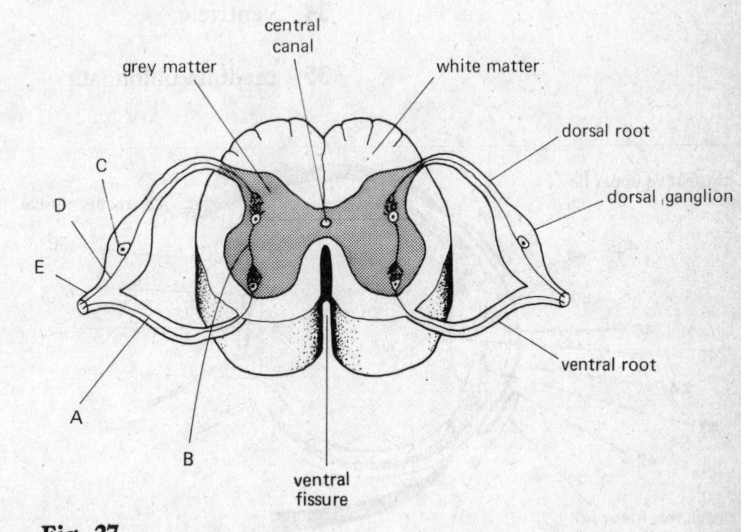

Fig. 27

16 Write down all the letters in the correct order through which an impulse would pass if a hot plate were dropped.
17 Name two receptors stimulated in the skin by the hot plate.
18 What part of this spinal cord would later conduct impulses to the brain for information?
19 Why is a reflex action always rapid?
20 What is the advantage of such rapid actions as in question 16?
21 Name the parts labelled A, B and D.
22 What accounts for the colour of grey matter?
23 What causes the swelling of the dorsal root ganglion?
24 What fluid is found in the central canal?
25 Name the bony structure protecting the spinal cord.

Consider the following experiment and answer questions 26 and 27. During an experiment, a section of the spinal cord of a frog was anaesthetised in the region of the thoracic vertebrae.

26 What response would you expect if a pin was stuck in the hind leg?
27 Is the frog likely to feel the pin?

Read the following account and then answer questions 28 to 30. Young kittens are observed to kill mice. Given a supply of 6 week old kittens, kept in isolation from birth, design an experiment to investigate whether this mouse killing action is
28 involuntary or voluntary.
29 inborn or learned.
30 What kinds of reaction would you expect your results to show?

Match the following pairs so that the number in front of the named part of the brain is beside the letter describing its function.

31 pituitary	A allows conscious thought.
32 cerebellum	B helps control growth
33 cerebral hemispheres	C receives impulses from the skin
34 ventricle	D co-ordinates balance and posture
35 medulla oblongata	E contains nutrient for brain cells

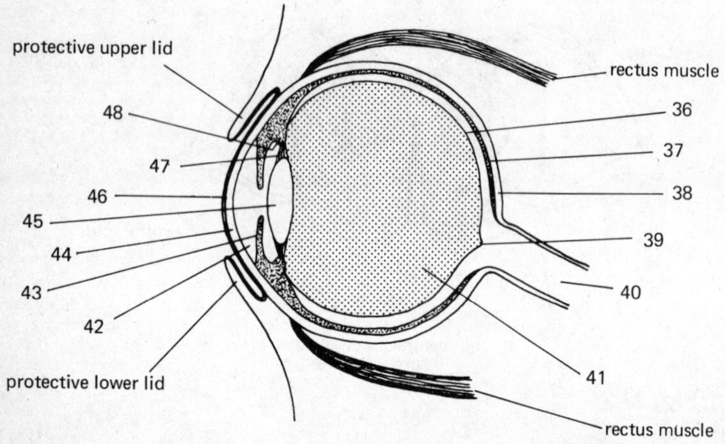

Fig. 28

Examine the diagram in Fig. 28 of a vertical section through the eye and name the parts numbered **36, 37, 38, 39, 40, 41, 42, 43, 44, 45, 46, 47** and **48.**

Read the following sentence and answer questions 49 to 54.
A boy reading a book in a dimly lit classroom lifts his eyes up to look out at an aeroplane in the bright sky.
49 Which rectus muscle will contract?
50 What happens to his pupils?
51 What happens to the part labelled 43?
52 What happens to the part labelled 45?
53 What happens to the part labelled 47?
54 What happens to the part labelled 48?
55 What is the reason for the name of part 39?
56 What is the function of parts 37, 38 and 40?
57 Which part of the eye has the light rays focused on it for the most distinct vision?
58 Why are colours so difficult to detect in dim light?
59 How does the focusing of a camera differ from that of an eye?

60 What kind of lens is needed to correct long sight?
61 Which vitamin is essential for the correct functioning of part 36?
62 What is the effect on vision of a deficiency of this vitamin?
63 Name one food which would prevent this deficiency?.
64 Name one disease of the eye caused by micro-organisms.
65 What defect of the eye often occurs in old age?

Examine the diagram of the ear in Fig. 29 and write down the names of the parts labelled **66, 67, 68, 69, 70, 71, 72, 73, 74, 75, 76** and **77.** What stimulus is detected in
78 part 73?
79 part 72?
What is the function of
80 part 67?
81 part 77?
82 Why should you not poke sharp objects such as a pencil into your ear?
83 People who fly in aeroplanes are sometimes told to swallow when they have temporary deafness. What is the purpose of this?

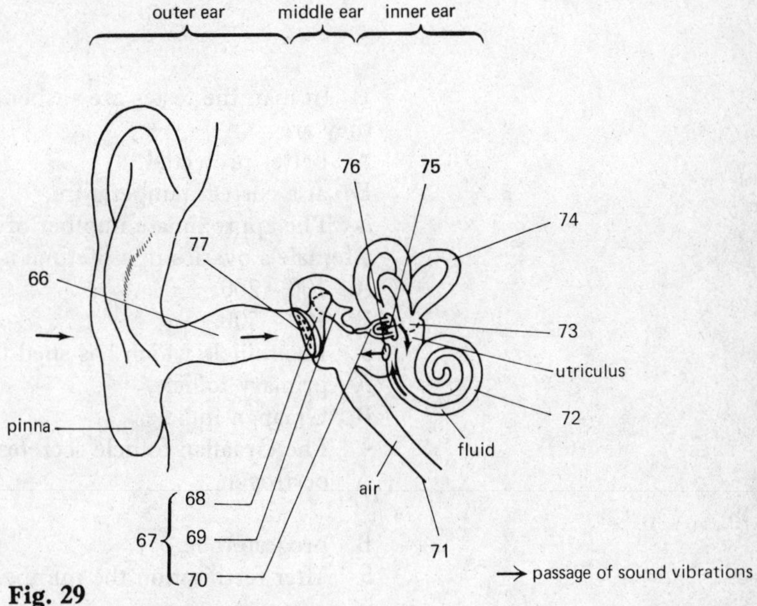

Fig. 29

84 Why do we experience dizziness after spinning around quickly several times?
85 Why can wax in the ear cause temporary deafness?
86 Which part of the ear does not function normally in astronauts in outer space?

Complete the following table by writing beside the numbers from it, the effects of either over or under secretion of the hormones and the names of the glands secreting them.

Hormone	Gland	Effect of under-secretion	Effect of over-secretion
phyone	pituitary	**87**	**88**
thyroxine	**89**	**90**	**91**
adrenaline	adrenals	—	**92**
luteinising	**93**	—	**94**

11 Reproduction

1 In man the testes are suspended in the scrotum and as a result they are

A better protected. C kept free from anti-bodies.
B at a correct temperature. D given better support.

2 The approximate number of ova which will be released from a female's ovaries in a lifetime is of the order of

A 100 – 200. C 700 – 800.
B 400 – 500. D 1 000 – 1 100.

3 The follicle which has shed the ovum from the ovary forms a

A primary follicle. C corpus luteum.
B Graafian follicle. D mature follicle.

4 The Graafian follicle secretes the hormone

A oestrogen. C F.S.H. (Follicular Stimulating Hormone)
B progesterone. D L.T.H. (Luteotropic).

5 After fertilisation the number of chromosomes in the zygote is

A the same as in the spermatozoon.
B twice as many as in the spermatozoon.
C half as many as in the spermatozoon.
D the same as in the ovum.

6 The sex of a female baby is determined by the presence of

A a Y chromosome. C two X chromosomes.
B an X and a Y chromosome. D two Y chromosomes.

7 The genes on a chromosome are composed of

A de-oxyribose nucleic acid. C chromatin.
B nuclease. D ribose nucleic acid.

8 The interval of time between fertilisation and birth is called

A parturition. C gestation.
B ovulation. D lactation.

9 After childbirth a hormone controlling milk production is released called

A a luteinising hormone. C prolactin.
B oestrogen. D a luteotropic hormone.

10 Mammalian reproduction is fundamentally different from most other animals because mammals

A produce more eggs. C nourish through a placenta.
B have more yolk in their eggs. D have external fertilisation.

Complete the following sentences by filling in the gaps with the most suitable words.
The male gamete called the **11** fuses with the female gamete called the **12** in the process of **13**. The cell so formed is a **14** and this divides into a ball of cells called the **15** which differentiates later into the **16**. Just before birth the maternal **17** gland secretes the hormone **18** which starts the involuntary contraction of the **19** muscles. These break the **20** membrane so the fluid escapes and the baby emerges assisted by the mother pushing down on her **21**

Examine Fig. 30. Name the parts of the male reproductive organs numbered **22, 23, 24, 25, 26, 27, 28** and **29.**
Give the numbers of the parts on the diagram in Fig. 30 which have the following functions.
30 secrete fluids to provide a medium for the sperm
31 transports sperms and urine
32 transports sperms only
33 transports urine only
34 enters the vagina during copulation
35 produce sperms

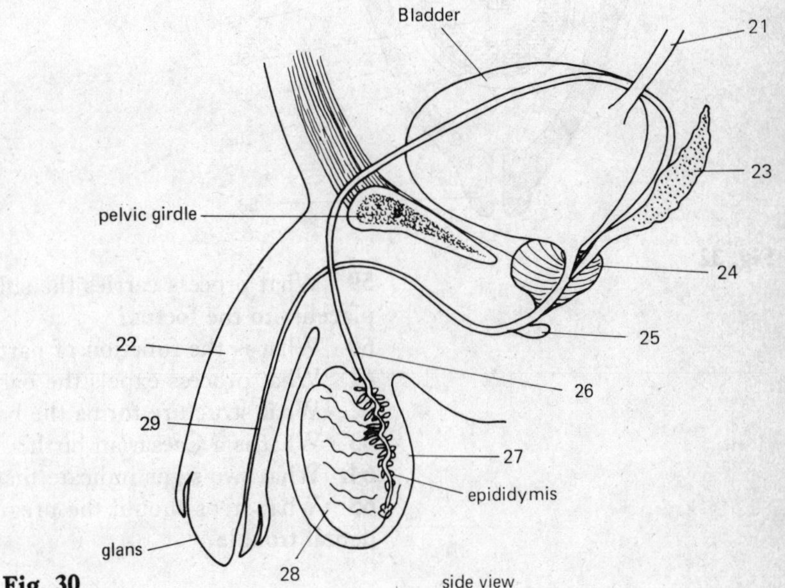

Fig. 30

Examine Fig. 31. Name the parts of the female reproductive organs numbered **36, 37, 38, 39** and **40.**

Give the numbers of the parts on the diagram which have the following functions.
41 produce ova
42 provide the normal site for fertilisation
43 initially receive sperms
44 allow implantation

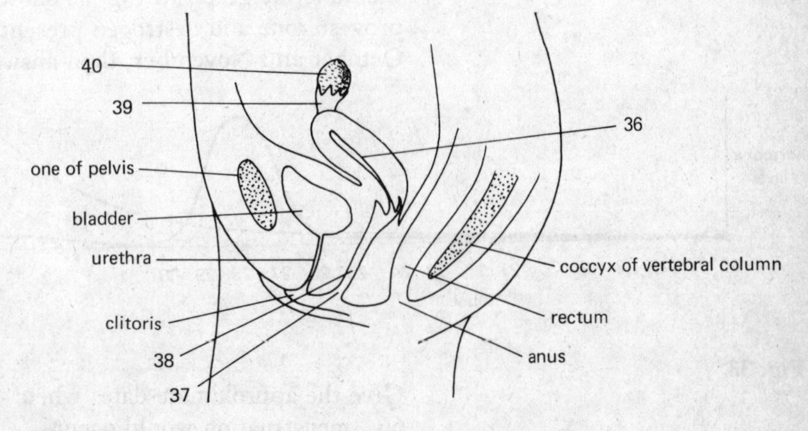

Fig. 31

45 Examine the above diagrams in Fig. 30 and Fig. 31 and starting from the part where sperms are produced, list in order the numbers of the structures through which the sperms will pass until one successfully fertilises the ovum after intercourse.

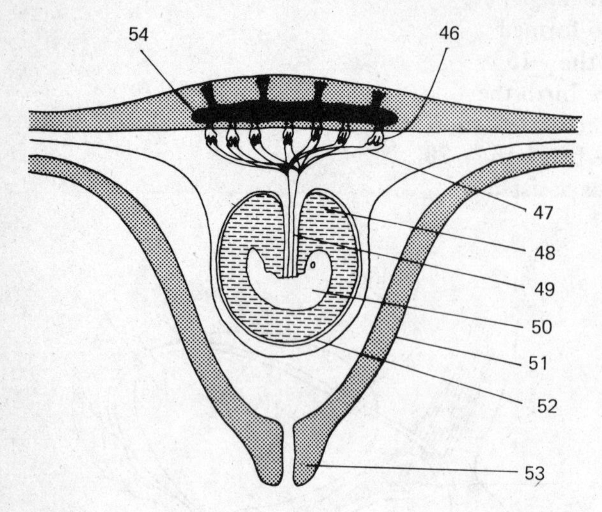

Fig. 32

Name the parts on the diagram in Fig. 32 of the developing human embryo numbered **46, 47, 48, 49, 50, 51, 52, 53** and **54.**

55 What structures are found in part 49?

56 Name two substances passing from the mother to the foetus.

57 Name two substances passing from the foetus to the mother.

58 By what physical process do these substances pass across the placenta?

59 What process carries the substances in question 56 from the placenta to the foetus?

60 What is the function of part 48?

61 What process expels the baby at birth?

62 What structure forms the baby's navel?

63 What is a Caesarian birth?

64 What two signs indicate that childbirth will shortly occur?

65 What steps should the pregnant mother take to prevent dental trouble?

Examine the graph in Fig. 33 showing the levels of the hormones progesterone and oestrogen present in a woman during part of October and November, then answer questions 66 to 72.

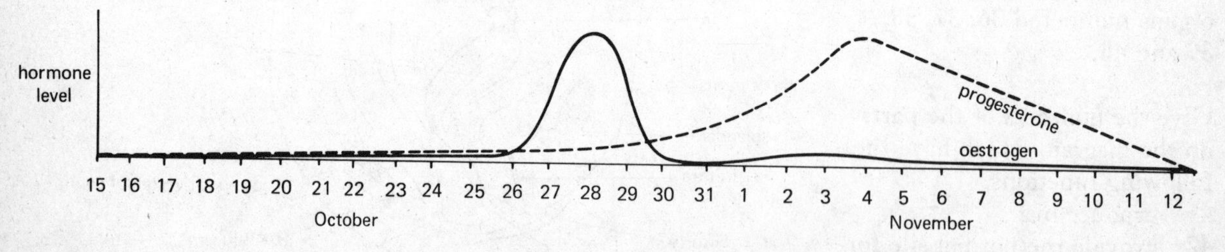

Fig. 33

Give the approximate dates when

66 menstruation would occur.

67 ovulation would occur.

68 the uterus wall thickens.

69 sexual intercourse could produce fertilisation.

70 implantation could occur following fertilisation.

71 How would this graph differ if pregnancy occurred during this period of time?
72 During which dates would a slight rise in body temperature be recorded?
73 Name two common venereal diseases.
74 What kind of organisms cause these diseases?
75 How are these organisms transmitted?
76 Which organs do they first affect?
77 How could a young baby be infected with venereal disease?

Match the following pairs by writing down the number in column X beside the letter from the correct definition in Column Y .

X		Y	
78	puberty	A	discharge of the lining of the uterus
79	lactation	B	cutting of the skin over the glans
80	menstruation	C	creation of new individuals without reproductive cells fusing
81	fertilisation	D	release of the egg into the fallopian tube from the ovary
82	asexual reproduction	E	period of time when secondary sexual characters develop
83	ovulation	F	features distinguishing the sexes other than reproductive organs
84	secondary sexual characters	G	period between fertilisation and parturition
85	differentiation	H	milk secretion by mammary glands
86	circumcision	I	fusion of male and female gametes
87	gestation	J	formation of specialised parts in structure

Apart from an increase in size, describe two structural changes occuring in boys (**88** and **89**) and two changes occurring in girls (**90** and **91**) during adolescence.

12 Inheritance and Population

1 The basis for work in heredity was provided by the experiments of
A Darwin. C Mendel.
B Malthus. D Pasteur.

2 The number of chromosomes in a human body cell is
A 12. C 46.
B 23. D 69.

3 If the zygote contains two genes carrying the same instructions for the character they control, the condition is referred to as
A genotypic. C heterozygous.
B phenotypic. D homozygous.

4 A person will be rhesus negative if he or she is
A lacking one chromosome.
B lacking one gene.
C homozygous with rhesus dominant genes.
D homozygous with rhesus recessive genes.

5 An individual's phenotype is **not** usually affected by
A possession of a single recessive gene.
B possession of a single dominant gene.
C the genotype as a whole.
D insufficient vitamins in the diet.

6 An example of a sex-linked disease is
A malaria. C haemolysis.
B leishmaniasis. D haemophilia.

7 In most developing countries the highest death rates are recorded between the ages of
A 0 and 1 year. C 60 and 65 years.
B 2 and 5 years. D 65 and 70 years.

8 The most important data for estimating the net reproductive rate is the
A crude birth rate. C specific fertility rates.
B age composition of females. D age distribution histogram.

9 Identical twins are produced from
A two ova fertilised by the same sperm.
B two sperms penetrating the same ovum.
C an ovum dividing before fertilisation.
D a zygote dividing after fertilisation.

10 The expanding population does **not** usually produce a problem of

A pollution.
B food shortage.
C more producers.
D more consumers.

The ability to curl up the two sides of the tongue is controlled by a single pair of genes with curling dominant to non-curling. Work out the possible genotypes (genetic constitutions) of parents who can have children of both curling and non-curling types. Then complete the following table by writing the correct symbols or description alongside the number on the lines. It will be easier to copy the table below and fill in your answers.

Let the gene for curling = C and the gene for non-curling = c

	Cross 1	Cross 2
Type of parents i.e. **curling** or **non-curling** (phenotype)	**11** __ × __	**12** __ × __
Genes possessed by parents (genotype) i.e. **CC Cc** or **cc**	**13** __ × **14** __	**15** __ **16** __
Gene in the gametes i.e. **C** or **c**	**17** __ __ **18** __	**19** __ __ **20** __ __
Offspring's genes (genotype)	**21** __ **22** __	**23** __ **24** __ **25** __ **26** __
Type of offspring (phenotype) i.e. **curling** or **non-curling**	**27** __ **28** __	**29** __ __ __ **30** __

The ability to taste the chemical phenylthiourea is controlled by a single pair of genes, with tasting dominant to non-tasting. A married couple can both taste this chemical but one of their parents in each case could not taste the chemical. Work out the genetic constitution of the married couple and show the variety of genotypes their children could possess by writing the correct symbols or description beside the numbers from the following table.

Let the gene for tasting = T, the gene for non-tasting = t.

	Possibility 1		Possibility 2	
Phenotype of married couples parents	Taster ×	Non-taster	Taster ×	Non-taster
Possible genotypes of the married couples parents	**31**	**32**	**33**	**34**

Married couples phenotype	Taster		×	Taster
Married couples genotype	35			36
Genes in their gametes	37	38	39	40
Offsprings genes (genotype)	41	42	43	44
Offsprings phenotype	45	46	47	48

Very rarely in the population, albino individuals are born to parents who both carry the recessive harmful gene for this character. Albinos have a complete lack of pigment and show no coloration in their skin, hair and irises.

49 What two special precautions will albinos need to take in their everyday lives, due to a lack of pigment?

What is the theoretical proportion of albino children who would be born to parents

50 who both carry one recessive gene?

51 one carrying and one not carrying one recessive gene?

52 one albino and one carrying one recessive gene?

In a population there are found to be 1 in 60 adults who carry the recessive gene. Consider the situation where marriage is completely at random, and then answer the following questions.

53 What are the chances of two recessive individuals marrying?

54 What proportion of children in the population will be albinos?

55 What advice could you give to the children of an albino parent married to a normal person?

56 How many of these children will be albinos themselves?

The inheritance of the blood groups A, B, AB and O is (in its simplest form) controlled by single genes which form the antigens on the red cells. The genes for A and B are dominant to O, while A and B together show no dominance.
Complete the following table.

Parents genotype	Possible genotypes of the offspring	Possible blood groups (phenotypes) of the offspring
AA × AO	**57**	**58**
BO × BO	**59**	**60**
AB × AO	**61**	**62**
AO × BO	**63**	**64**

Complete the following table by writing down beside the numbers from
Column 1 antigen A, B, A and B, or none.
Column 2 antibody a, b, a and b, or none.
Column 3 either agglutination, or mixes.
(A knowledge of genetics is not required for this question)

	1	2	3			
Blood group of recipient	Antigen on red cell	Antibody in serum	Effect of donors blood from group			
			A	B	AB	O
A	**65**	**66**	**67**	**68**	**69**	**70**
B	**71**	**72**	**73**	**74**	**75**	**76**
AB	**77**	**78**	**79**	**80**	**81**	**82**
O	**83**	**84**	**85**	**86**	**87**	**88**

The chart in Fig. 34 shows the inheritance of a certain kind of disease. Individuals who suffer from this are dwarfs. The symbol D represents the dominant gene for normal growth and d the recessive gene for the dwarf character.
Write alongside the numbers in the chart, the genotypes of the individuals and state whether they will show normal growth or a dwarf-like appearance. The last line is complete to help you work out the others.

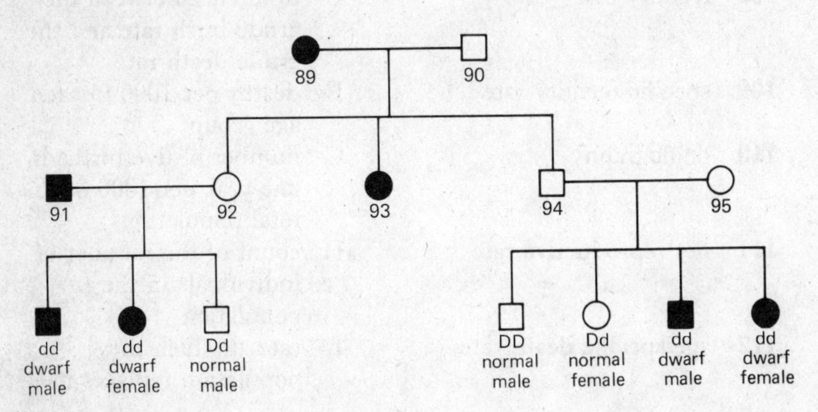

Fig. 34

96 Give one reason why a family tree such as is shown in Fig. 34 would be very unlikely.

A certain kind of colour blindness is sex-linked.
97 What does sex linkage mean?
98 Why are women less frequently colour blind than men?
99 What is a carrier?

Complete the following chart by writing alongside the number on the lines (i) the sex, (ii) the genotype, (iii) the phenotype, (colour vision or colour blind).

Phenotype	Colour vision female				Colour blind male	
Chromosomes	XX				XY	
Genotype	Cc				c–	
Gametes	ova	CX	cX	sperm	cX	–Y
		100	**101**		**102**	**103**

Match the following pairs by writing down the number from column X beside the relevant letter from column Y.

	X		Y
104	census	A	number of deaths in one year per 1000 of the total population
105	crude birth rate	B	number of live births in one year in each 5 year age group of women
106	crude death rate	C	study of population numbers
107	rate of natural increase	D	number of live births in one year per 1000 of women aged 15–45
108	fertility rate	E	difference between the crude birth rate and the crude death rate
109	specific fertility rate	F	deaths per 1000 in each age group
110	demography	G	number of live births in one year per 1000 of the total population
111	net reproductive rate	H	count of the number of individuals in the population
112	age specific death rate	I	rate at which the population replaces itself

The diagrams opposite in Fig. 35 provide some statistics about the population living on a small island, and should be used to find answers to questions 113–126.

113 What is the name given to the kind of diagrams shown in Fig. 35.

114 What is the total number of males in the population?

115 What is the total number of females in the population?

116 What was the total population on the 1st January, 1975?

117 What was the total population on the 31st December, 1975?

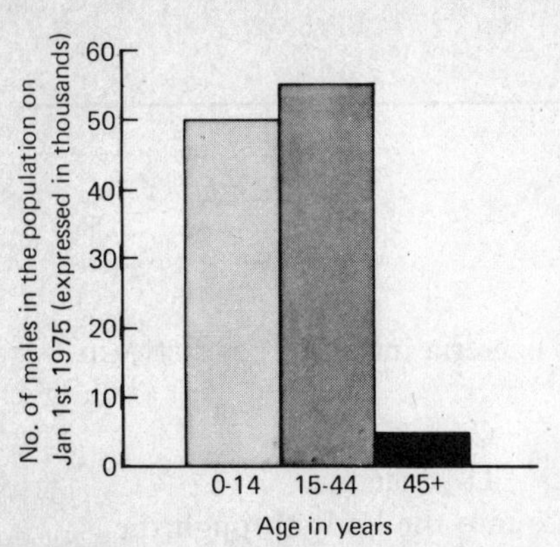

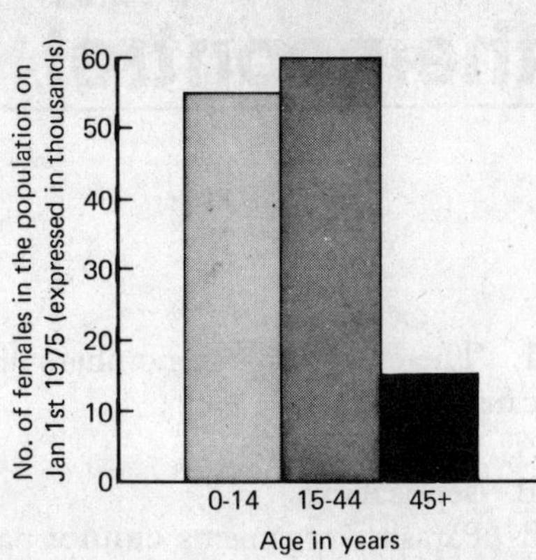

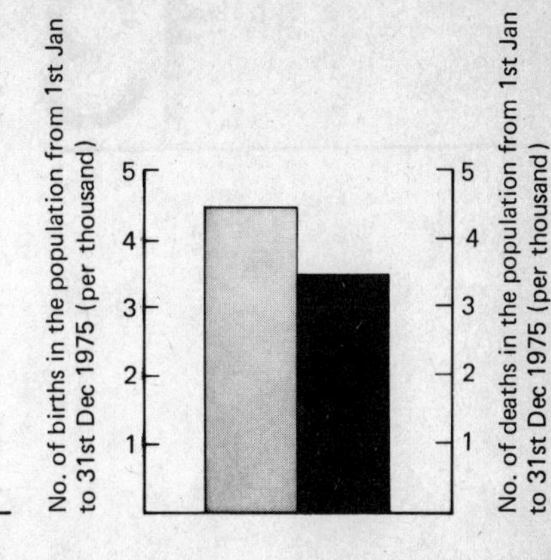

Fig. 35

118 Calculate the crude birth rate.
119 Calculate the crude death rate.
120 What is the rate of natural increase for the population?
121 Calculate the fertility rate.
122 Is this population expanding, contracting or remaining the same size?
123 Give the reason for your previous answer.
124 Give one hypothesis to account for the lower population in the 45 + age group.
125 Give one hypothesis to account for the large difference in numbers between the males and females in the 45 + age group?
126 Give one hypothesis to account for the reduction in the population of the 0–14 age range.

13 Disease Organisms and their control

1 The entry of large numbers of bacteria into the blood stream causes
A inflammation.
B septicaemia.
C haemolysis.
D anaemia.

2 Parasitic organisms **cannot** pass into the body through the
A skin.
B hair.
C respiratory system.
D alimentary canal.

3 Which of the following is the commonest disease vector?
A insects.
B algae.
C bacteria.
D fungi.

4 Organisms **unlikely** to be parasitic in man are
A bacteria.
B fungi.
C algae.
D protozoa.

5 Bacteria will survive
A freezing.
B boiling.
C concentrated phenol.
D antibody combination.

6 A feature **unlikely** to be found in bacteria is
A reproduction by spores.
B reproduction by division.
C a distinct nucleus.
D a mucilaginous coat.

7 Pasteur showed that micro-organisms
A cause malaria.
B are killed by antibiotics.
C destroy silk worms.
D form lung tubercles.

8 The purpose of the 'booster' second injection is to
A increase the number of antibody secreting lymphocytes.
B add serum antibodies to the body from the 'booster'.
C start antibody secretion in the body.
D make the body resistant to additional diseases.

9 Vaccines are prepared by
A using dead or weakened pathogens
B synthesising chemicals.
C extracting red blood cells.
D distillation of sea weed.

10 An antibiotic of fungal origin is
A Sulphonamide.
B Penicillin.
C Quinine.
D Nilodin.

The diagrams in Fig. 36 show three parasites of man.
Name these organisms.

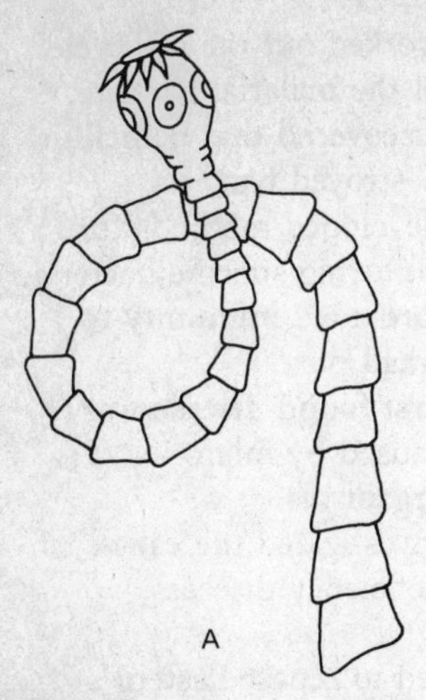

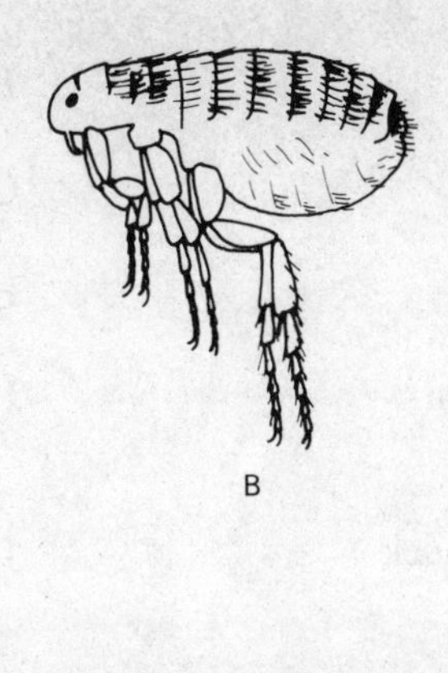

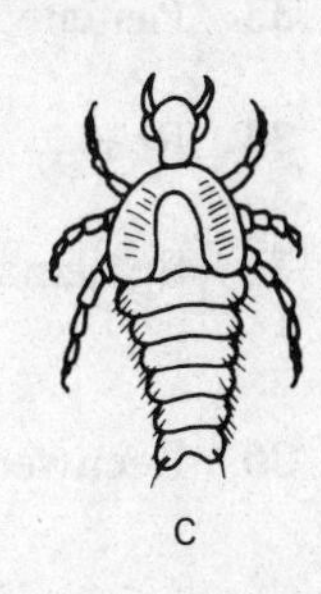

Fig. 36

11 A
12 B
13 C

Complete the following table by writing beside the numbers, where these organisms are found, the parts they use to attach to the body and where they lay their eggs.

	Where found	Parts to attach to the body	Eggs laid
A	**14**	**15**	**16**
B	**17**	**18**	**19**
C	**20**	**21**	**22**

23 What diseases are transmitted by B?
24 What diseases are transmitted by C?
25 What are the symptoms of a person with parasite A?
26 What is a parasite?

Match the name of scientist with the work for which he was famous, by writing down the number from column X beside the letter from column Y.

X		Y	
27	Fleming	A	performed the first experiments to disprove spontaneous generation.
28	Gowland-Hopkins	B	first used antiseptics.
29	Jenner	C	worked out the life cycle of filariasis.
30	Koch	D	first discovered micro-organisms.

31	Lister	E	worked out the life cycle of the malarial parasite.
32	Manson	F	discovered that penicillin destroyed bacteria.
33	Pasteur	G	developed methods for culturing specific bacteria.
34	Ross	H	provided immunity to small pox.
35	Spallanzani	I	first found disease was caused by micro-organisms.
36	Leeuwenhoek	J	investigated the causes of deficiency diseases.

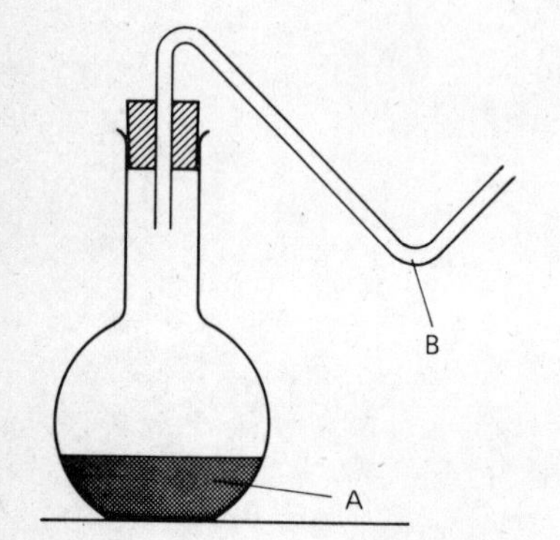

Fig. 37

The apparatus shown in Fig. 37 can be used to repeat Pasteur's experiment to disprove spontaneous generation. Examine this apparatus and answer questions 37 to 45.

37 What is the meaning of spontaneous generation?
38 Label parts A and B.
39 What is the purpose of part B?
40 What other apparatus is needed for this experiment?
41 Why is A first boiled in the flask?
42 Give the results of this experiment.

What result would you expect if drops were streaked onto sterile agar plates and then incubated, from
43 part A?
44 water added to part B?
45 Besides disproving spontaneous generation what other conclusion can you derive from this experiment?

Examine the following data and answer questions 46 to 51.
A suspension of bacteria was poured into four tubes to which different concentrations of phenol were added. The results are shown in the table.

Tube	Conc. of phenol	Results seen 1 week later
A	0·02%	slowly became cloudy
B	0·03%	became cloudy more quickly than A
C	0·05%	remained clear
D	full strength	remained clear

46 What causes some tubes to appear cloudy?
47 In which tubes were the bacteria killed?
48 Which of the above concentrations of phenol would you choose to treat a wound?
49 Explain why you would not choose the other concentrations to treat wounds

50 Which scientist first used this kind of method to treat wounds?
51 What method has largely replaced this kind of wound treatment at the present time?

Examine the following data and answer questions 52 to 57.
From the following figures plot the graph showing the number of divisions per hour by bacteria maintained at different temperatures. (Graph paper needed.)

Temperature °C	0	10	15	20	25	30	35	40	45	50
Number of divisions/hour	0	0	0·5	1	1·5	2·0	2·5	3·0	3·0	0

52 How do you account for the lack of division below 10°C?
53 Between what temperatures is growth at a maximum?
54 Why are there no divisions at 50°C?
55 Why do the number of divisions of the bacteria give a measure of their growth?
56 Suggest one reason why the bacteria used in this experiment could be parasitic in man.
57 What is the meaning of the term bacteriostasis?

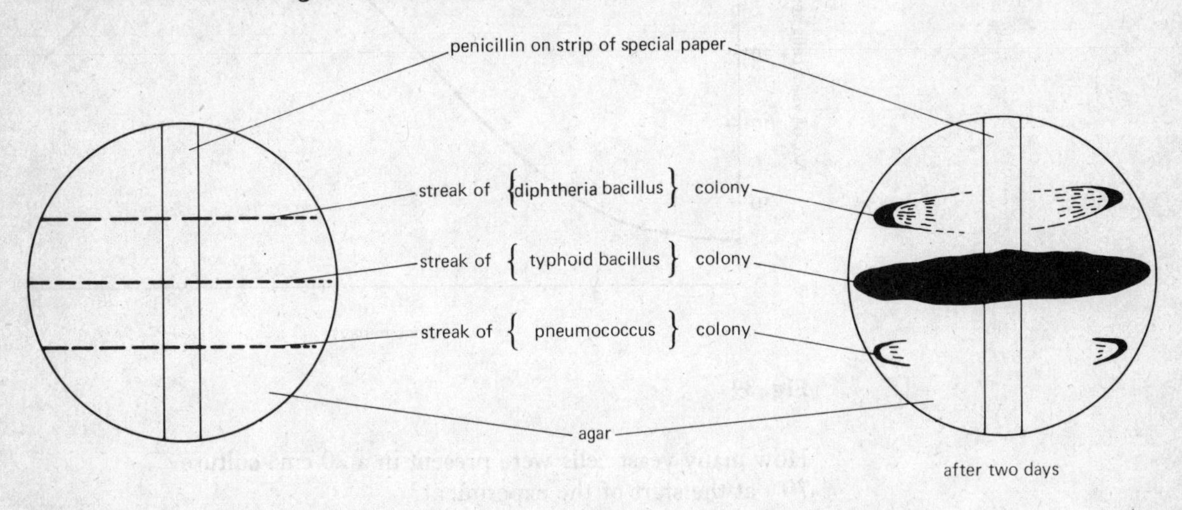

Fig. 38

The diagram in Fig. 38 shows the effect of certain bacteria streaked onto sterile agar plates impregnated with a strip of penicillin.
58 Name the type of dish in which such an experiment is performed.
59 How are these glass dishes sterilised?
60 How are the streaks of micro-organisms made?
61 What is the best temperature at which to incubate these plates for growing bacteria?
62 Name the scientist who first developed these techniques for growing and culturing bacteria.

63 What special precautions are required to be taken during these experiments?
64 Which of these bacteria are most resistant to penicillin?
65 Which of these bacteria are least resistant to penicillin?
66 How would you expect the *Pneumococcus* colonies to differ after a further day? Give reasons for your answer.
67 Name one other disease organism killed by penicillin.
68 By mistake, the top was removed from a similar plate set up as above and left at 28°C. What would you expect to observe?
69 How does the shape of the bacterium causing typhoid differ from that causing pneumonia?

Examine the following data and answer questions 70 to 80.
The number of yeast cells in a tube of nutrient kept at a constant temperature is shown in the graph Fig. 39.

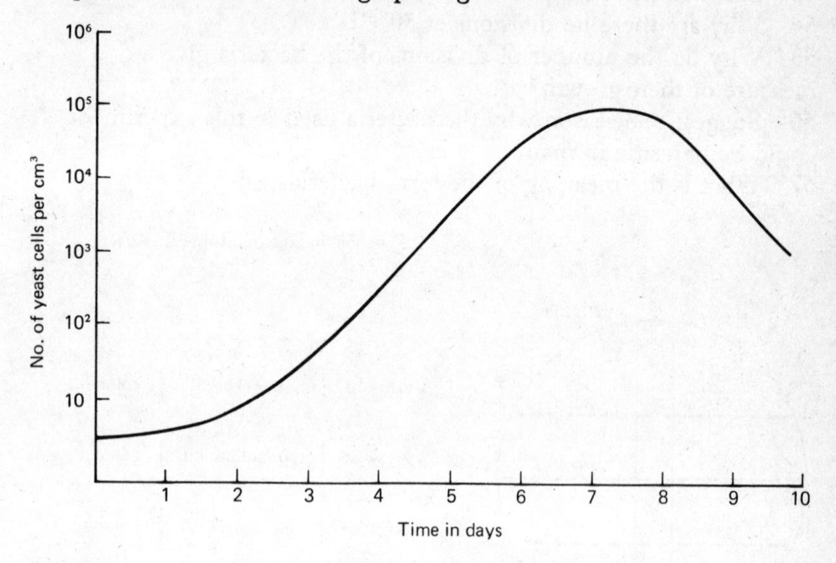

Fig. 39

How many yeast cells were present in a 20 cm³ culture
70 at the start of the experiment?
71 after 3½ days?
72 at their maximum?
73 What could account for the slow initial growth?
74 Give two hypotheses to explain the reduction in growth after 7 days.
75 Apart from water, what else must the culture contain in order to allow growth?
76 Name the gas evolved.
77 How would you test this gas?
78 What else is produced besides the gas?
79 What kind of organism is yeast?

80 Name one food or other product in which yeast is used during its manufacture.

Examine the graph in Fig. 40 and the data supplied and answer questions 81 to 90.

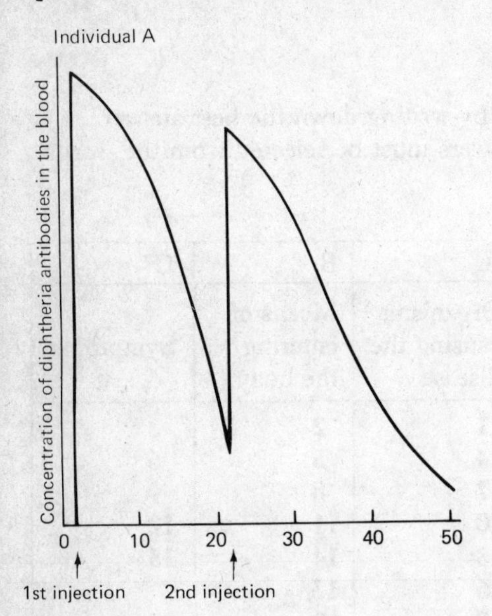

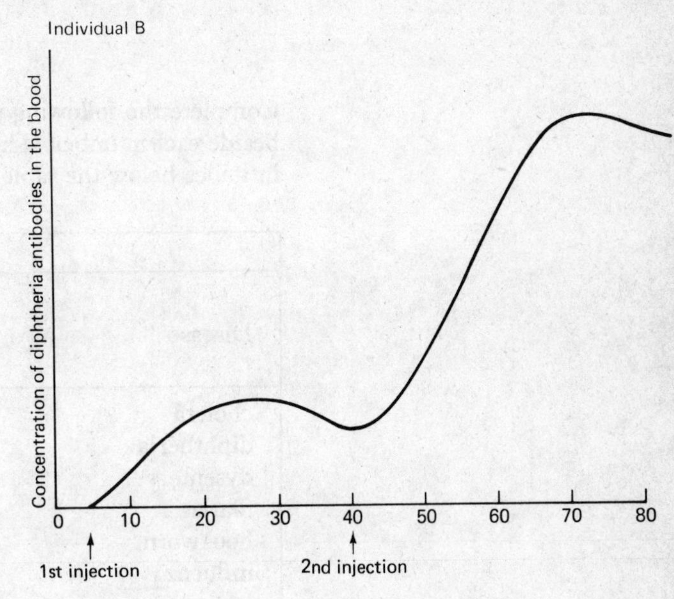

Fig. 40

The graphs show the concentration of diphtheria antibodies over a period of days in the blood of two individuals A and B each given two injections, although A had a different inoculum from B.

81 What was injected into individual A?
82 What was injected into individual B?
83 Why did the level of antibodies generally continue to rise in B?
84 What kind of immunity did A receive?
85 Why was there a delay before antibodies were found in B?
86 Which cells make antibodies?
87 What is the function of an antibody?
88 When would the two kinds of injection shown in A and B above be given together?
89 How was the inoculum in A prepared?
90 How was the inoculum in B prepared?
91 What is the second injection in B called?

14 Disease and its Transmission

Complete the following table by writing down the best answer beside each number. The answers must be selected from the words in italics below the table.

	A	B	C
Disease	Organisms causing the disease	Means of entering the body	Symptoms
cholera	1	2	3
diphtheria	4	5	6
dysentery	7	8	9
filariasis	10	11	12
hookworm	13	14	15
influenza	16	17	
leprosy	18	19	20
leptospirosis	21	22	23
malaria	24	25	26
ringworm	27	28	29
roundworm	30	31	
schistosomiasis	32	33	34
sleeping sickness	35	36	37
smallpox	38	39	40
tuberculosis	41	42	43
typhoid	44	45	46
venereal disease	47	48	49
whooping cough	50	51	52
yaws	53	54	55
yellow fever	56	57	58

Best answers to be selected from
column A: *virus bacterium fungus protozoan helminth*
column B: *food contact air insect bite skin in water*
column C: *diarrhoea sores red patch red spots throat-inflammation coughing anaemia yellow skin blood in faeces swollen lymph glands*
(Choose one answer only, although some alternatives are acceptable.)

The diagram in Fig. 41 illustrates the life cycle of *Schistosoma*. In questions 59 to 68, select the alternative which best completes the sentence. Questions 59 to 64 refer directly to Fig. 41.

59 Sexual reproduction commonly occurs in the life cycle at stage

A W. C Y.
B X. D Z.

60 Asexual reproduction commonly occurs at stage

A W. C Y.
B X. D Z.

61 The best way of controlling the parasite at stage W is to

A immunise with anti-schistosome vaccine.
B properly dispose of the faeces.
C take drugs such as nitrothiozole.
D take purgatives.

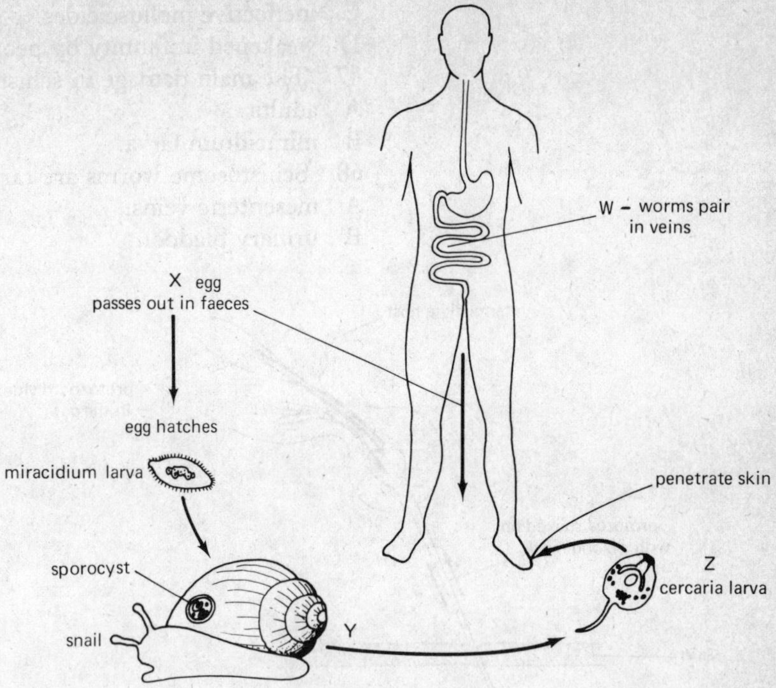

Fig. 41. Life cycle of Schistosoma

62 The best way of controlling the parasite at stage X is to

A stock infested water with fish.
B avoid drinking infected water.
C use proper sanitation.
D avoid bathing in infected water.

63 The best way of controlling the parasite at stage Y is to

A provide more irrigation channels.
B wear shoes.
C use molluscicides.
D spread Nilodin on grass.

64 The best way of controlling the parasite at stage Z is to

A boil drinking water.
B spray oil on water.
C remove weeds from water.
D avoid bathing in infected water.

65 The snail is best described as

A a carrier. C a causative agent.
B a reservoir. D an intermediate host.

66 The main reason for the large increase in people suffering from schistosomiasis is the

A increased crop irrigation.
B ineffective drugs.

C ineffective molluscicides.
D weakened immunity by people carrying worms.

67 The main damage in schistosomiasis is caused by the
A adults.
B miracidium larva.
C cercaria larva.
D eggs.

68 Schistosome worms are rarely found in the
A mesenteric veins.
B urinary bladder.
C small intestine.
D stomach.

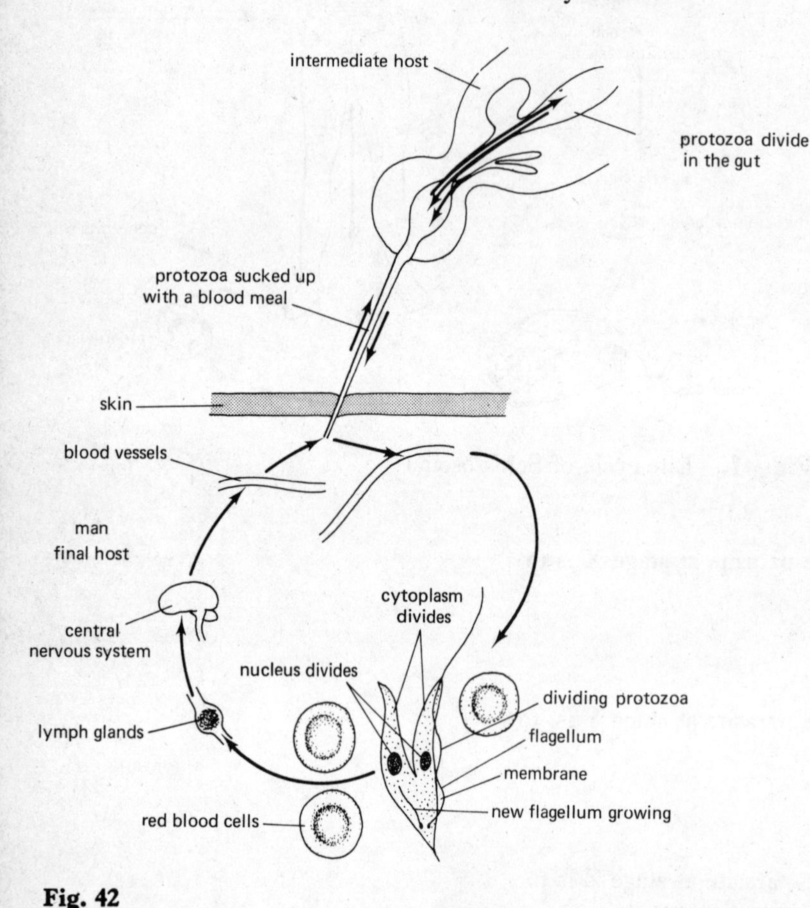

Fig. 42

Examine the diagram in Fig. 42 showing the life cycle of a disease protozoan, and answer questions 69 to 79.

69 Name this protozoan.
70 On what does this protozoan feed?
71 What part does this protozoan use to move in the body of the host?
72 What disease is caused?
73 How does this organism upset the control of the body by the brain?
74 What treatment is given to a disease sufferer?
75 Why is such treatment not always successful?
76 Name the disease vector.
77 Where are the parasites stored prior to the vector biting the host?
78 Where do the larval stages of the vector develop?
79 Why do wild animals make the control of this disease so difficult?

Examine the following sentence and answer questions 80 to 91.
A man had a regular fever with profuse sweating every 72 hours, followed by cold shivering spells and headaches and he also suffered from anaemia.

80 Name the disease from which he is suffering.
81 Name the parasite causing this disease.
82 Name one drug which he should take on medical advice.
83 What causes the fever?
84 What causes the anaemia?
85 What is the best way of eradicating this disease from a community? (details not required).

86 How do you check that an individual is not a carrier of this disease?
87 Where does the sexual phase in the reproductive cycle of this parasite occur?
88 This is a benign example of a disease. What does that mean?
In the control of this disease, what is the purpose of
89 spraying oil on the surface of water?
90 introducing fish to stagnant water?
91 infected people sleeping under nets?

Write down the number and beside it the correct answer from those provided in italics in the table. Use each answer only once.

Name of vector	Disease transmitted	Distinguishing feature	Method of destroying vector
housefly	**92**	**93**	**94**
Anopheles mosquito	**95**	**96**	**97**
Aedes mosquito	**98**	**99**	**100**
Culex mosquito	**101**	**102**	**103**

Examples	Examples	Examples
yellow fever	*white stripes*	*spray oil on water*
malaria	*body settling at* 30° *to skin*	*remove rubbish*
cholera	*body settling parallel to skin*	*stock water with fish*
filariasis	*lobed-mouth parts*	*remove stagnant water*

15 Social Hygiene

1 International laws compel all countries to report outbreak. of certain (notifiable) diseases, but these do **not** include

A tuberculosis.
B typhus.
C smallpox.
D cholera.

2 The outbreak of a single apparently unconnected disease is described as

A sporadic.
B endemic.
C epidemic.
D pandemic.

3 Ventilation will **not** be assisted by

A convection.
B conduction.
C aspiration.
D louvred windows.

4 Ventilation does **not** help to

A increase the evaporation of sweat.
B remove humid air.
C make respiration easier.
D reduce air-borne infections.

5 Water **cannot** be made fit for drinking by

A heating.
B distillation.
C adding chlorine.
D boiling.

6 Bacteria are **not** destroyed in water during its purification at a water works by

A grid screens.
B protozoa.
C sunlight.
D addition of chlorine.

7 Water storage tanks are built high above the houses in a town because

A here they are less likely to become infected.
B this is the easiest storage method.
C rainfall collects in high places.
D water finds its own level for distribution.

8 Man does **not** obtain water from the sea for the irrigation of his crops, because sea water makes

A the plant cells become turgid.
B water leave the plant cells by osmosis.
C the uptake of sodium ions destroy the plant cells.
D the uptake of chlorine ions destroy the plant cells.

9 The use of human sewage as a fertiliser **cannot** be responsible for the transmission of

A hookworms. C cholera.
B filarial worms. D typhoid.

10 The onset of tuberculosis **cannot** be detected by
A the Mantoux test. C coughing blood.
B periodic X-rays. D blood tests.

11 Tuberculosis most commonly affects the
A testis. C blood system.
B lungs. D nervous system.

12 Immunity to tuberculosis is provided by the injection of
A vaccinia. C T.B. toxin.
B B.C.G. D T.B. serum.

13 The hookworm *Ancylostoma* is most commonly found in the
A duodenum. C liver.
B colon. D hepatic veins.

14 Hookworm eggs hatch into larvae which moult and then pass into
A a snail. C a fish.
B a pig. D the skin.

15 A disease carrier is a person who
A has recovered from a disease.
B shows no symptoms but possesses the disease organisms.
C is incapable of catching the disease.
D carries the symptoms of the disease.

Examine the map of a small town in Fig. 43 and answer questions 16 to 25.

16 State five faults (not more than one sentence on each) with the planning of this town from a public health aspect.

The crosses represent cases of cholera reported in a recent outbreak. The dots represent cases of malaria reported over a longer period of time.

17 Where do you think the source of the cholera outbreak was found?

18 By what test would they verify the source of the cholera organisms?

19 Explain three essential courses of action to be taken by the health authorities to prevent further infection from cholera.

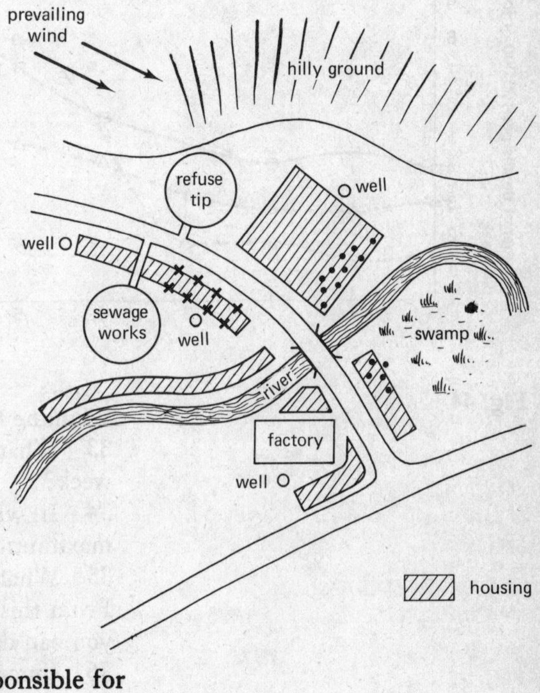

Fig. 43

20 What is the title generally given to the person responsible for supervising medical aspects of such a disease outbreak?

21 Suggest why the malarial patients were found in one particular part of the town.

22 Explain **three** essential steps to be taken to reduce the incidence of malaria in this town.
23 Why do the people living near the swamps find the heat so oppressive?
24 Suggest a better position for their houses and explain the reason for such a move.
25 Name **three** ways in which ventilation can be improved in the houses.

Examine the following paragraph and answer questions 26 to 32. Some of the houses in this tropical town were poorly constructed. Explain (not more than one sentence for each) one disadvantage produced by the following faults in construction.
26 mud floors
27 lack of a damp proof course
28 all wooden supports
29 absence of cavity walls
30 dark coloured roof
31 absence of air bricks
32 absence of ceiling vents

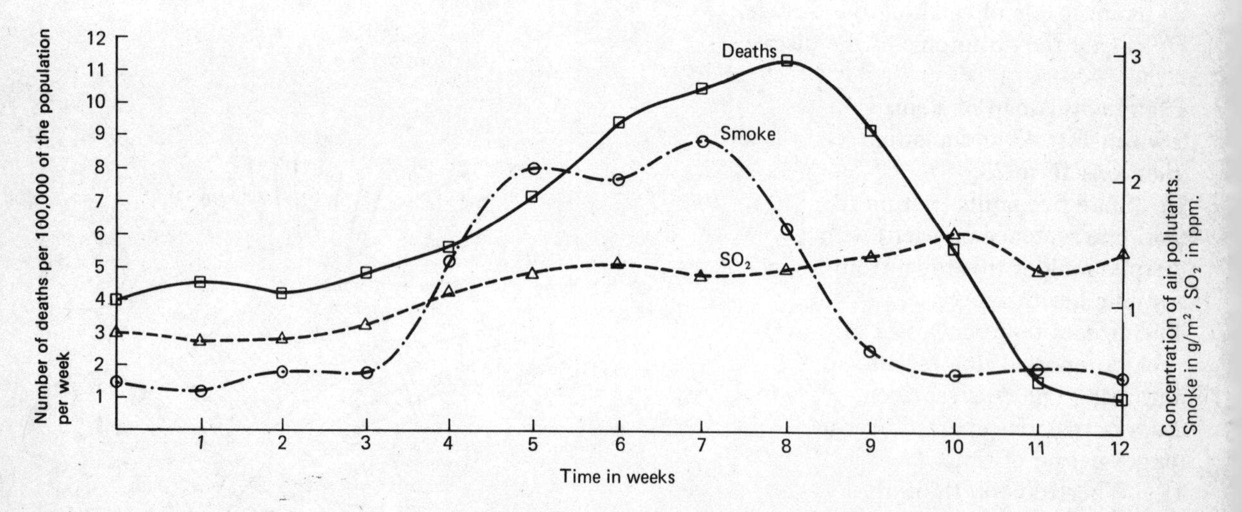

Fig. 44

Examine the data in Fig. 44 and answer questions 33 to 43.
33 What was the maximum number of deaths recorded in one week?
34 In which week did the concentration of SO_2 reach a maximum?
35 What is SO_2?
From this graph explain the reasons for any relationships which you can deduce between the death rates and
36 concentration of SO_2?
37 the concentration of smoke.
38 Explain the meaning of the units g/m³ and ppm.

39 Can you suggest any reason for the lower death rates in weeks 11 and 12 when compared with weeks 1 and 2?
40 Suggest the kinds of diseases resulting in the deaths which increased in the weeks 6 to 9.
Explain why a greater proportion of the deaths occurred among
41 coal miners.
42 heavy smokers.
43 Do you think these figures were obtained from a rural, small urban, or large urban area?

Examine the following data and answer questions 44 to 49.
In an area in which sleeping sickness, filariasis, malaria and yellow fever are known to occur, large numbers of flying insects were caught. A microscopic examination revealed *Trypanosoma* parasites in *Glossina* and *Culex*, and *Wuchereria* parasities in *Anopheles* and *Culex*. *Plasmodium* parasities were found in *Anopheles* only.
Which insects spread
44 sleeping sickness?
45 malaria?
46 filaraisis?
47 Why were the organisms causing yellow fever not found?
48 If the whole population can be kept free from sleeping sickness for a period longer than three months, the disease will be eliminated from this area. Why is this so?
49 Does the 'population' in the above question have to include all the mammals in the area? Explain your answer.

Raw sewage, on its way from the houses to the sewage works, passes through the following parts of the sewage system. Explain beside the number for each part, its function in the process of sewage disposal. (No more than one sentence for each.)
50 U-bend in the water closet
51 sewer pipes
52 the grid or screen
53 grit pit
54 sedimentation tanks
55 sludge tanks
56 percolating filters
57 coke beds
58 humus tanks
59 nearby rivers

The following statements are either always true (T) always false (F) or true only sometimes (S). Write beside the number of the question, the correct letter T, F or S accordingly.
60 The water in clouds is derived from or formed by the evaporation of the water from the land, surface waters or vegetation.

61 Bacteria are harmful to man.
62 Bile is produced in the gall bladder.
63 Euthanasia will improve the human race by controlling human inheritance.
64 The danger of taking drugs is that they cause addiction.
65 Heavy smoking causes coronary disease.
66 A pathogen is an organism which transmits disease.
67 Mosquitoes spread filariasis.
68 The lungs serve partly as excretory organs.
69 Muscles work by contraction only.
70 Eating uncooked meat causes hookworm disease.

Examine the following data and answer questions 71 to 83.
The most common diseases detected in men in three prisons A, B and C are shown in the table below. Numbers represent prisoners recorded as suffering from the disease over a five year period.

	Prison		
	A	B	C
hookworm	0	15	0
dysentery	0	8	1
beri-beri	0	0	25
yellow fever	0	10	0
bronchitis	20	11	2
scabies	0	12	0
tuberculosis	15	4	3
lung cancer	8	0	1
liver fluke	0	0	8
coronary thrombosis	10	4	0

Examine the types of the various diseases in each prison. Explain (giving one reason in each case) which of these prisons is most likely to
71 provide a deficient diet, mainly of milled rice.
72 have unhygienic food preparation.
73 have given uncooked fish to eat.
74 have dirty bedding, infrequently changed.
75 have the highest incidence of smoking among the prisoners.
76 be found in an advanced industrial country.
77 be found in West Africa or South America.
78 provide insufficient exercise for the prisoners.
79 have the prisoners working in heavy air pollution.
80 have the prisoners working on digging irrigation channels.
81 have nearby mosquito breeding grounds.
82 have inadequate ventilation.

83 For each prison describe the particular prophylactic (preventitive) action that should be taken by the prison authorities in order to control the specific disease concerned. Do not consider actions to be taken at a prison where less than four prisoners have suffered from the disease.

16 Answers

Instructions for marking

1 Allow one mark for the answer to each numbered question, unless the answer is followed by a higher mark shown by a figure in brackets.
2 Words separated by / in the mark scheme show where parts are divided to gain separate marks.
3 Alternative answers are separated by the word *or*.
4 Answers in brackets are acceptable but they are not as good as the ones they follow.
5 Some longer type answers may be expressed in other words compared to those used in the scheme. Allow them provided the meaning is the same

Chapter 2 The activities, classification and evolution of organisms

1 D
2 C
3 B
4 A
5 E
6 F
7 F
8 B
9 D
10 A (C)
11 B
12 C
13 D
14 C
15 D
16 C
17 B
18 D
19 A
20 C
21 A 2 *or* 3 *or* 4 years.
B 11 *or* 12 *or* 13 years.
C 19 *or* 20 *or* 21 years. (3)
22 Childhood.
23 Adolescence.
24 Height.
25 Protein.
26 The average rate of growth in boys is greater during adolescence/and childhood/ adolescence growth starts earlier in girls. (2)
(Other answers exist but the best two are given above)
27 Some constriction of invertebral discs *or* loss of turgor with age.
28 Gestation (pregnancy).
29 Lack of food/disease (2) (accept named protein foods and correctly named diseases.)
30 Fertilisation.
31 Voice breaking *or* growth of beard *or* increased muscle growth.
32 Species.
33 Darwin.
34 Linnaeus.
35 *Proconsul.*
36 Phylum.
37 Bacterium.
38 Fungi (bacteria).
39 Arthropods.
40 Hookworm.
41 *Schistosoma.*
42 Vertebrates.
43 Trypanosome *or* sea anemone *or* earthworm *or* locust.
44 Amphibian *or* frog.
45 Invertebrates lack a backbone *or* vertebrae.
46 Single-celled *or* acellular *or* non-cellular.
47 Can live on land and in water *or* larval stages are aquatic.
48 Locust/eats man's crops. (2)
49 Trypanosome/destroys man's red blood cells *or* causes sleeping sickness. (2)
50 Earthworm/breaks up the soil *or* takes leaves or humus into the soil. (2)
51 Body temperature fluctuates with that of the surroundings. *or* body temperature does not remain constant.
52 Flagellum/legs/wings. (3)
53 Animal because it catches food with tentacles (other answers exist).
54 Respiration.
55 Feeding *or* nutrition.
56 Excretion *or* elimination of waste materials.
57 and **58** Any two from respond to a stimulus, reproduce, grow, have cells.

59 Organic.
60 Chlorophyll.
61 Light.
62 Photosynthesis.
63 Carbon dioxide.
64 Hair.
65 Mammary gland.
66 Thumb.
67 Lips.
68 Navel *or* scar of umbilical cord.
69 Protection *or* insulation *or* beautification.
70 To help in chewing *or* assist in speech.
71 Mammals.
72 Young borne alive/care of young, *or* constant body temperature. (2)
73 Produce milk for the young offspring.
74 Frees the arms for other activities/than movement. (2)
75 The enlarged forebrain/the young suckling from the mother/strong maternal instinct. Any 2 (2)
76 800 million years (+ or — 50 million years).
77 Amoeba, tapeworm, housefly, fish, frog, reptile, bird, mammal. (Deduct 1 mark for each incorrectly placed animal up to a maximum of 3.) (3)
78 Bones/the hard parts of the body such as scales and teeth. Imprints left in the mud. Any 2 (2)
79 Ancestors lived in trees/ where the bodies were more likely to decompose after death. (Other answers possible) (2)
80 The bi-pedal habit.
81 Mentally *or* culturally.

Total 96
(excluding question 1)

Chapter 3 Food

1 A
2 A
3 C
4 B
5 B
6 B
7 D
8 C
9 D
10 C
11 A
12 C
13 A (B)
14 A
15 C
16 C
17 C
18 B
19 D
20 B
21 B
22 C
23 B
24 D
25 A
26 D
27 C
28 Milk is essential for healthy growth.
29 The milk contains vitamins essential for growth.
30 Milk casein supplies protein *or* both diets contain casein.
31 Iron.
32 Vitamin C *or* Ascorbic Acid.
33 Hopkins.
34 Night blindness *or* beri beri *or* dermatitis *or* scurvy, *or* rickets (accept others).
35 C
36 B
37 C
38 C
39 D
40 Embryo *or* germ.
41 They are removed.
42 B_1.
43 Beri-beri.
44 Protein.
45 Starch *or* carbohydrate.
46 In the leaves (stem).
47 Photosynthesis.
48 Rice.
49 Par boiled (process explained).
50 Water soluble, *or* vitamin destroyed at high temperatures (allow both).
51 Contains starch and reducing sugar. Lacks protein/and fat. (4)
52 Non-reducing sugar.
53 Reducing sugar.
54 Change it (hydrolysed) to a reducing sugar.
55 Litmus colour change *or* add sodium bicarbonate until effervescence stops.
56 Iron *or* vitamin B_{12}.
57 Phosphorus *or* calcium *or* vitamin D.
58 Iodine.
59 Protein.
60 Vitamin A.
61 Vitamin B_2.
62 Vitamin B_1.
63 Vitamin B_2.
64 Vitamin C.
65 Tube F.
66 Bacteria and fungi (2 marks) *or* micro-organisms.
67 Canning *or* bottling.
68 Fruit etc.—variety of answers.
69 Pickling *or* vinegar adding.
70 Onions etc—allow variety.
71 Salting.
72 Meat etc.
73 Dehydrating *or* drying.
74 Fish *or* potatoes etc.
75 They become inactive.
76 Micro-organisms require water to live.

77 Reduce carbohydrate and fat.
78 Plenty of protein/iron/ phosphorus/calcium/vitamin D. (2 marks each for any 2 facts stated.)
79 Protein in beans/peas/soya beans/etc. (2 marks each for any 2 facts stated.)
80 More carbohydrate/and fat/plenty of drink. (2 marks each for any 2 facts stated.)
81 Reduce carbohydrate/and fat. (2 marks each for any 2 facts stated.)
82 Bread has a high energy content *or* each g has enough heat energy to raise the temperature of 240 litres of water 1°C.
83 The rate of body activity while at complete rest *or* activity to maintain essential processes only while at rest.
84 $\frac{5 \times 100 \times 4{\cdot}2}{2} = 1050$ joules/g
85 $40 \times 10 \times 9{\cdot}8$ joules = 3920 joules = 3·9 kJ. (2)
86 1 g of sugar contains 16 kJ of which muscle can use 4 kJ/ Thus 1 g approximately of sugar will be needed. (2)
87 Processes involved in the B.M.R./e.g. heart beat etc. (2)
88 Warmth may activate heat resistant bacteria.
89 Vitamin D.

Total 100

Chapter 4 Source and supply of food

1 D
2 A
3 A
4 D
5 C
6 D
7 D
8 A
9 A
10 A
11 Grass, snail, bird, cat, (Any example) (4)
12 All plants *or* autotrophs.
13 All herbivores.
14 All carnivores.
15 Their growth is slow *or* more difficult to feed *or* more wasteful of energy.
16 Carbohydrate *or* sugars *or* glucose *or* starch.
17 and 18 Water and carbon dioxide.
19 Sunlight *or* light.
20 Chlorophyll.
21 Oxygen.
22 Respiration.
23 Nitrates.
24 Carbohydrates *or* sugars.
25 Amino.
26 Oxygen for respiration is produced during photosynthesis.
27 Nitrogen fixing bacteria/in soil/nitrates/plant protein/eaten. *or* lightning form oxides of nitrogen *or* bacteria/in legumes. (Any 5 points) (5)
28 Plant *or* named water plant e.g. *Hydrilla or Ceratophyllum.*
29 Oxygen is released during photosynthesis.
30 Re-lights a glowing splint.
31 The same experiment in the dark.
32 Increases the rate of bubbling *or* photosynthesis.
33 Increased temperature.
34 Heavy particles settle first.
35 Air/organisms. (2)
36 Dead *or* decaying/plants and animals *or* organic matter. (2)
37 Provides mineral salts *or* improves crumb structure.
38 Erosion by wind/poor anchorage/easily leached. Any 2 (2)
39 Cold for plant growth/ waterlogged/lacks air. Any 2 (2)
40 Silt and clay would flocculate.
41 Fertile soil for plant growth/soil parts balanced. (2)
42 Limewater *or* bicarbonate indicator.
43 Turns limewater cloudy *or* indicator yellow.
44 With baked soil/to kill micro-organisms. (2)
45 Decay humus/fix nitrogen. (2)
46 Rain to wash away surface humus *or* roots no longer bind the soil.
47 Exposure of soil to washing away *or* blowing away.
48 The surface soil film is destroyed/water runs off taking surface layers away. (2)
49 Washes out mineral salts.
50 Cold *or* waterlogged/ lacking air. (2)
51 Prevent rain washing away the humus.
52 Retain surface soil/because some trees always present. (2)
53 Water erosion of surface layers.
54 Bind the soil/and return nitrates to the soil. (2)
55 Building of walls *or* levelling in strips/to prevent water run off. (2)
56 Absorbed by plants.

57 More plant food for fish *or* fish prey.
58 Remove samples of the pond water/place in containers kept in the same conditions/1 container control/1 with nitrate added/1 with phosphate/place in fish and measure growth at intervals. (6)
59 Dams/pumps/ditches *or* channels. (3)
60 Any named water borne disease e.g. Schistosomiasis (bilharzia).
61 Prevents loss of weight/by reducing respiration. (2)
62 Maximum growth is up to 3 months *or* growth is less in the 3 to 6 month period.
63 More economic because food fully utilised *or* reduces faeces.
64 Growth increased by hormones such as thyroxine.
65 Protein needed for growth.
66 Population increases at an geometric rate/while the food supply only increases at an arithmetic rate. (2)
67 Starvation *or* food supply insufficient.
68 More food produced by modern farming methods.
69 Birth control/death due to war/and disease. (3)
70 Demography

Total 100

Chapter 5 The Alimentary Canal

1 D
2 B
3 D
4 B
5 D
6 C
7 C
8 D
9 A
10 A
11 D
12 A
13 B
14 C
15 C
16 A
17 B
18 B
19 C
20 D
21 Ptyalin.
22 Gingivitis.
23 Goitre.
24 Carrier.
25 Ascorbic acid.
26 Chyme.
27 Symbiosis.
28 Pyloric sphincter.
29 Absorption.
30 Assimilation.
31 Enamel.
32 Pulp cavity.
33 Dentine.
34 Cement *or* periodontal membrane.
35 Periodontal membrane *or* cement.
36 Hold the tooth firm.
37 Blood vessels *or* nerves.
38 Acids made by bacteria acting on the food, destroy enamel.
39 Foetus uses the calcium *or* phosphate *or* vitamin D required for tooth growth.
40 Fluoride.
41 More cusps *or* not chisel shape *or* not present in the milk set.
42 Removes food from between the teeth *or* less likely to damage the gums *or* strengthens the gums.
43 Blue.
44 Enzyme destroyed by boiling *or* starch present.
45 Blue.
46 No enzyme to change the starch *or* starch present.
47 Brown.
48 Enzyme in saliva breaks down starch *or* starch absent.
49 Blue colour remains *or* no colour change.
50 No reducing sugar present.
51 Blue colour remains *or* no colour change.
52 No reducing sugar present.
53 Red.
54 Reducing sugar present.
55 Rate would slow down.
56 Stop the reaction *or* prevent the pytalin from working.
57 Convert the starch to sugar.
58 Hydrolysis.
59 Amylase is produced in the pancreas.
60 Churn up the food *or* mechanical digestion.
61 It is protein.
62 Hydrochloric acid alone.
63 Stomach wall.
64 Produced by living cells *or* always protein in nature.
65 Blue.
66 Alkaline bile salts *or* sodium bicarbonate.
67 Tube A/yellow. (2)
68 Formation of fatty acids.
69 Emulsifies the fats in milk/ produces an alkaline medium.(2)
70 Liver.
71 Pancreas.

72 Yellow due to hydrochloric acid present.
73 Blue due to bile and pancreatic juice *or* sodium bicarbonate.
74 Yellow as bacteria make acids.
75 Oesophagus.
76 Liver.
77 Gall bladder.
78 Duodenum.
79 Caecum.
80 Anus.
81 Rectum.
82 Ileum *or* small intestine.
83 Colon *or* large intestine.
84 Pyloric sphincter.
85 Ileum *or* 82.
86 Stomach.
87 Pancreas *or* liver *or* 76.
88 Colon *or* large intestine *or* 83.
89 Inflammation.
90 Store bile.
91 Contain faeces.
92 Peristalsis.
93 Spleen *or* diaphragm.
94 Pancreatic juice.
95 Maltase/converts maltose to glucose. (2)
Sucrase/converts sucrose to glucose and fructose. (2)
Lactase/converts lactose to glucose and galactose. (2)
Enterokinase/activates trypsin. (2)
Erepsin/converts dipeptides to amino acids. (2) Any 2 (4)
96 Amino acids.
97 Glucose.
98 Blood capillaries.
99 Hepatic portal.

Total 104

Chapter 6 Respiration

1 B
2 A
3 E
4 C
5 B (D)
6 D
7 A
8 C
9 E
10 A
11 D
12 D
13 A
14 C
15 Yeast *or* some bacteria *or* other named examples.
16 and **17** Alcohol and carbon dioxide.
18 Fermentation.
19 Zymase.
20 Fructose *or* carbohydrate.
21 Thyroid cartilage (larynx).
22 Alveoli *or* air sacs.
23 Bronchus.
24 Pleural membranes.
25 Trachea.
26 Lung.
27 Diaphragm.
28 Warm *or* moisten *or* filter the air.
29 Prevent entry of particles *or* food down the trachea.
30 Prevent the trachea from collapsing.
31 Contract to help inspiration *or* make thorax air tight.
32 Pharynx, trachea, bronchus, bronchioles, alveoli.
33 Air not changed *or* stagnant air.
34 Tubercles *or* scars.
35 By X-rays *or* radiography.
36 Toxins from bacteria *or* bacteria *or* phagocytes surrounding bacteria.
37 Coughing.
38 Pneumonia *or* influenza *or* bronchitis *or* cancer *or* pleurisy *or* asthma, etc. Any 2 (2)
39 Less disease organisms in fresh air *or* the air containing the disease organisms is removed.
40 Bronchus.
41 Lung.
42 Rib cage *or* thorax wall.
43 Diaphragm.
44 They inflate.
45 Pressure reduced.
46 Inspiration.
47 They contract.
48 Ribs *or* intercostal muscles.
49 Intercostals/and diaphragm. (2)
50 Iron lung *or* respirator.
51 Carbon dioxide.
52 Oxygen.
53 Nitrogen.
54 Length of $CO_2 = 0{\cdot}8$ cm. /% of $CO_2 = \frac{0{\cdot}8}{20} \times 100$/ = 4% (3)
55 Length of $O_2 = 3{\cdot}2$ cm. /% of $O_2 = \frac{3{\cdot}2}{20} \times 100$/ = 16% (3)
56 Expired air.
57 Expired air is warmer and/ contains more water vapour. (2)
58 The breathing rate is increased by the concentration of carbon dioxide/in the blood which stimulates the brain. (2)
59 The main discomfort is due to increased humidity/preventing the evaporation of sweat/ causing overheating. (3)
60 It is impossible to blow all the air out of the lungs/ residual air remains. (2)
61 $16 \times 1{\cdot}5 \times \frac{4}{100} = 0{\cdot}96$ l ($960\ cm^3$) (2)
62 $15 \times 1{\cdot}3 \times \frac{4}{100} = 0{\cdot}78$ l ($780\ cm^3$) (2)
63 Man X was heavier, consequently did more work.

Man Y had better muscle tone. (2)
64 Breathing would be deeper and/faster. (2)
65 More breaths per minute and/more air exchanged. (2)
66 Lack of oxygen *or* low air pressure.
67 Inactivates cilia.
68 Increases likelihood of contracting lung cancer *or* chronic bronchitis *or* causes breath shortage *or* increases mucus production.
69 Removal of phlegm *or* mucus/since cilia are damaged. (2)
70 Spirometer.
71 Tracing to top dotted line.
72 Tracing to bottom dotted line.
73 Longer tracings and/more per minute. (2)
74 B
75 Place insect/separated from the potassium hydroxide in the boiling tube./ Put fluid in the capillary tube/measure its movement in a given time./ Control alongside/lacks an insect/apply correction accordingly./ Fluid movement indicates rate of oxygen uptake./ Potassium hydroxide absorbs CO_2. (9)
76 Activity of the insect may vary at different times./ Insect activity may cause heat production. (2)
(Other alternatives can be deduced.)

Total 103

Chapter 7 Circulatory system
1 A
2 B
3 B
4 D
5 D
6 C
7 A
8 D
9 B
10 A
11 T
12 T
13 S
14 F
15 S
16 T
17 T
18 F
19 S
20 F
21 F
22 E
23 B
24 G
25 D
26 I
27 C
28 A
29 J
30 H
31 Right auricle.
32 Chordae tendinae (tendons).
33 Right ventricle.
34 Left ventricle.
35 Bicuspid valve.
36 Left auricle.
37 Pulmonary veins.
38 Pulmonary artery.
39 Aorta
40 Inferior vena cava.
41 Prevent flow of blood back into the right auricle.
42 Support the valve *or* prevent valve flaps from being forced into the auricle.
43 Transport blood to the lung.
44 De-oxygenated.
45 Contract to force blood all round the body.
46 Cardiac.
47 Does not fatigue *or* capable of regular contractions.
48 31
49 Coronary artery.
50 Reduced.
51 Blue appearance/due to mixing of oxygenated and de-oxygenated blood. (2)
52 Carotid arteries.
53 Pulmonary artery.
54 Hepatic vein.
55 Aorta.
56 Renal artery.
57 Hepatic portal vein—liver—hepatic vein—vena cava—heart *or*—RA—RV—pulmonary artery—lung—pulmonary vein—heart *or*—LA—LV—aorta—femoral artery. (3)
Deduct 1 mark for each omission.
58 From the lungs to the heart.
59 Thinner/less elastic/contains valves/less muscular. Any 3 (3)
60 Leg muscle contractions/valves/*or* blood pressure. (3)
61 Increases.
62 Less oxygen/more carbon dioxide/more dissolved foods *or* named foods. (3)
63 Pulsating flow *or* increased flow *or* flowing under pressure.
64 Vena cava.
65 Carotid artery *or* 52.
66 Between 85 and 95 minutes.
67 Between 0 and 10 minutes.
68 Between 35 and 60 *or* 65 minutes.
69 Between 10 and 35 minutes.
70 0 to 10 minutes.
71 Peristaltic gut movements/respiratory movements. (2)

72 95 + *or* — 2.
73 Adrenaline.
74 Recovery from exercise.
75 50 and 65 minutes.
76 Strengthens heart muscle/prevents fat deposition in vessels/exercises muscles of heart and arteries. Any 2 (2)
77 Increased carbon dioxide detected by the brain.
78 Oxygen/and glucose *or* respiratory substrate *or* food. (2)
79 Stethoscope.
80 They would have all been greater.
81 Red blood cells.
82 Lymphocyte.
83 Phagocyte.
84 Phagocyte.
85 Enables it to squeeze through narrow capillaries.
86 Anaemia.
87 Haemoglobin.
88 Hormones/food/carbon dioxide/waste *or* named waste materials. (4)

Total 103

Chapter 8 The Skeleton
Several answers exist for questions 1 to 10 so that all alternatives are not covered. Some common answers are provided.
1 Answer given.
2 Skull/protects the brain *or* ribs/protect the lungs *or* heart, vertebrae/protect the spinal cord, pelvis/protects reproductive organs. (2)
3 Named muscle e.g. biceps/is attached to the radius and place of attachment, e.g. ulna *or* pectoral girdle. (2)
4 Skull pivots on/the vertebrae *or* ulna pivots on/the humerus. (2)
5 Any named movable joint, e.g. elbow joint/movement described e.g. bends. (2)
6 Any named bone/marrow. (2)
7 Any named structural part e.g. skull/shape of part, e.g. gives shape to the head or face etc. (2)
8 Bone matrix.
9 Sternum/nose/ear/pelvic girdle/invertebral disc/coccyx/etc. Any 2 (2)
10 Sternum allows breathing movements/pelvic girdle allows passage of baby *or* invertebral disc acts as cushion etc. (2)
11 Sacrum *or* sacral vertebrae.
12 Pelvis *or* pelvic girdle.
13 Femur.
14 Tibia.
15 Fibula.
16 Tarsals.
17 Metatarsals.
18 Pectoral girdle.
19 Carpals.
20 Metacarpals.
21 Gap called fontanelle in baby.
22 Sutures of the skull *or* pelvic girdle.
23 B
24 D
25 A
26 A
27 D
28 C
29 Calcium/phosphates. (2)
30 Vitamin D.
31 Pituitary hormone *or* named pituitary hormone *or* thyroxine *or* parathormone etc.
32 Atlas.
33 Cervical.
34 Thoracic/lumbar/sacral/coccyx. (4)
35 Thoracic—Facets/for rib articulation.
Lumbar—more projections *or* named projections/for muscle attachment.
Sacral—fused together *or* with pelvic girdle/for rigidity.
Coccyx—reduced structure/smooth for sitting. (8)
36 Centrum.
37 Vertebrarterial canals.
38 Transverse process.
39 Neural arch.
40 Neural canal.
41 Nodding *or* up and down *or* vertical.
42 Rotating *or* side to side *or* horizontal.
43 Spinal cord.
44 Artery *or* blood vessel.
45 Invertebral disc *or* cartilage/acts as a cushion *or* shock absorber. (2)
46 Cartilage.
47 Ligament.
48 Synovial fluid.
49 Ball *or* head.
50 Ball and socket.
51 Universal *or* rotation.
52 Synovial fluid/cartilage. (2)
53 Ligaments.

54 Arthritis.
55 Ligaments.
56 Hollow back.
57 Pentadactyl.
58 Periosteum.
59 Collagen.
60 Acetabulum.
61 Tone.
62 Chondrin.
63 Fulcrum.
64 Round shoulder.
65 Insertion.
66 Triceps.
67 Tendons *or* origins.
68 Humerus.
69 Scapula.
70 Biceps.
71 Radius.
72 Ulna.
73 Relax.
74 Contract.
75 Antagonistic.
76 Pivot *or* fulcrum *or* lever.
77 Hinge.
78 Pivot.
79 Ball and socket.
80 Impulse *or* nerve impulse.
81 Voluntary.
82 A.T.P.
83 A.D.P.
84 Load × distance from fulcrum = Effort × distance

$50 \times 40 = E \times 2$

$2000 = 2E$

$1000\text{ g} = E$ (3)

85 Third order lever.

Total 107

Chapter 9 Excretion and the Skin

1 T
2 S
3 N
4 N
5 S
6 S
7 N
8 T
9 N or T
10 N
11 S
12 N
13 N
14 N
15 N
16 S
17 S
18 S
19 S or T
20 T
21 D
22 C
23 E
24 J
25 G
26 A
27 F
28 B
29 H
30 I
31 B
32 A
33 C
34 A
35 C
36 C
37 A
38 A
39 C
40 C
41 *Evaporation* of sweat cools the body.
42 Undigested food is *egested* from the body in faeces. (Allow if the word excreted is changed.)
43 Traces of urea are *excreted* from the body in sweat. (Allow if the word secreted is changed.)
44 Cells in distilled water become *turgid*.
45 The liver stores glycogen but *not* protein. (Allow if protein is deleted.)
46 Cornified layer *or* stratum corneum.
47 Epidermis.
48 Dermis.
49 Papilla.
50 Follicle.
51 Erector muscle.
52 Sub-cutaneous fat (fat).
53 Sweat gland.
54 Sebaceous gland.
55 Malpighian layer.
56 Produce new cells.
57 Keep the skin (or hair etc) supple etc.
58 Increased activity *or* increased secretion of sweat.
59 They will dilate *or* more blood will flow through them.
60 In the malpighian layer.
61 Screen ultra violet light *or* prevents burning.
62 The skin wrinkles.
63 Acts as an insulator/provides respiratory substrate. (2)
64 Removes water vapour/so speeds up evaporation. (2)
65 Excessive sweating/in high temperatures and high humidity. (2)
66 Plenty to drink/plenty of salt. (2)
67 Palms of hand *or* soles of feet.
68 Provides extra protection.
69 Fungus.
70 Mite.
71 Thick *or* large air spaces *or* greasy fibres.

72 Trap air to act as an insulator in cool climates.
73 Fine fibres *or* light fibres.
74 Absorb sweat to produce cooling in warm climate *or* do not trap air so are cool in warm climates.
75 Very close mesh *or* artificial fibres.
76 Conduct heat rapidly from the body.
77 Glomerulus *or* knot of capillaries.
78 Bowman's capsule.
79 Loop of Henle.
80 Collecting duct.
81 Cortex.
82 Less oxygen/less water/less salts/less urea/more carbon dioxide. in efferent arteriole Any 2 (2)
83 Water reabsorbed by osmosis/in the loop of Henle./ Salts reabsorbed by active uptake/in the convoluted tubules. (4)
84 Water/salts/urea. (3)
85 Dialysis.
86 Pelvis—ureter—bladder—urethra. (4)
87 Solution A is more concentrated than solution B.
88 Solution A is more concentrated than the cell contents.
89 Osmosis.
90 The tissue would lose weight/as substances diffuse out to the lower concentration/ because the cell membrane becomes permeable. (3)
91 Clinical thermometer.
92 Hygrometer.
93 9 am
94 10.30 to 10.45.
95 30 *or* 31 *or* 32°C.
96 9 am to 9.15 am
97 9.30 am to 10.45 am
98 10.30 am to 10.45 am
99 10.15 *or* 10.30 to 10.45 am
100 Rise in body temperature/ fainting. (2)
101 Placed in cool *or* ice packs/ remove humid air. (2)
102 The high humidity.
103 Respiration/vaso constriction/shivering. (3)

Total 122

Chapter 10 The Nervous System

1 D
2 D
3 C
4 A
5 D
6 B
7 C
8 C
9 D
10 B
11 A
12 A
13 C
14 B
15 B
16 E D C B A E (do not insist on C or the last E). (3)
17 Oval *or* temperature receptors/pain receptors/ lamellated *or* touch receptors. Any 2 (2)
18 White matter.
19 The brain is not involved *or* they are involuntary *or* the spinal cord co-ordinates *or* no decision involved.
20 Protection from injury.
21 A. motor neuron *or* motor nerve. B. intermediate *or* connector *or* internuncial neuron. D. sensory neuron. (3)
22 Cell bodies.
23 Cell bodies.
24 Cerebro spinal fluid.
25 Vertebral *or* neural arch.
26 Withdrawal of the leg.
27 No
28 Give a choice of mice and food or other distractors/ observe if the kitten *always* attack the mice. (2)
29 Present young kittens with mice, and observe if they always kill /repeat after they have watched a cat kill mice. (2)
30 Voluntary learned action.

31 B
32 D
33 A
34 E
35 C
36 Retina.
37 Choroid.
38 Sclerotic.
39 Blind spot.
40 Optic nerve.
41 Vitreous humour.
42 Aqueous humour.
43 Iris.
44 Cornea.
45 Lens.
46 Conjunctiva.
47 Suspensory ligament.
48 Ciliary muscle *or* body.
49 The upper one.
50 Get smaller *or* contract *or* constrict.
51 Circular muscles contract to enlarge it *or* constricts the pupil *or* it enlarges.
52 Becomes less convex *or* thinner.
53 Becomes taut *or* stretched *or* has tension.
54 Relaxes.
55 Light is not detected here *or* retina absent.
56 40 carries impulses *or* messages to the brain.
38 supports *or* protects the eye *or* maintains shape.
37 supplies nutrient to the eye *or* reduces internal reflection. (3)
57 Fovea *or* yellow spot.
58 Cones *or* retinal cells detecting colour/are only stimulated at high light intensity. (2)
59 Eye lens changes shape/camera lens moves nearer or further from the film. (2)
60 Convex.
61 Vitamin A.
62 Night blindness.
63 Carrots *or* fish *or* liver *or* eggs *or* milk and its products.
64 Conjunctivitis *or* trachoma.
65 Presbyopia *or* old sight *or* loss of lens elasticity *or* cataract.
66 Auditory meatus *or* ear passage.
67 Ear ossicles.
68 Malleus.
69 Incus.
70 Stapes.
71 Eustachian tube.
72 Cochlea.
73 Ampulla.
74 Semi-circular canal.
75 Fenestra ovalis *or* oval window.
76 Fenestra rotunda *or* round window.
77 Tympanum *or* tympanic membrane.
78 Acceleration *or* movement.
79 Sound *or* vibrations.
80 Transmit vibrations.
81 Vibrate due to sound waves and move malleus.
82 May damage the tympanum.
83 Equalise pressure on either side of the tympanum.
84 False impulses sent to the muscles/by fluid movement in the semi circular canals. (2)
85 Prevents movement of the tympanum.
86 Gravity perceptors *or* the utriculus.
87 Infantilism *or* dwarf formation *or* retarded sexual development.
88 Gigantism *or* thickened skin.
89 Thyroid.
90 Stunted mental and physical growth.
91 Increases metabolic rate *or* body activities increase.
92 Increases activity of many body organs *or* named examples.
93 Pituitary.
94 Causes growth of corpus luteum.

Total 106

Chapter 11 Reproduction

1 B
2 B
3 C
4 A
5 B
6 C
7 A
8 C
9 C
10 C
11 Sperm *or* spermatozoon.
12 Ovum (egg).
13 Fertilisation.
14 Zygote (fertilised egg).
15 Embryo.
16 Foetus (baby).
17 Pituitary.
18 Oxytocin.
19 Uterus.
20 Amniotic.
21 Diaphragm.
22 Penis.
23 Seminal vesicle *or* vesicular seminalis.
24 Prostate gland.
25 Cowper's gland.
26 Vas deferens.
27 Scrotum.
28 Testis.
29 Urethra.
30 23, 24 and 25.
31 29
32 26
33 21
34 22
35 28
36 Uterus (womb).
37 Vestibule.
38 Vagina.
39 Fallopian tube *or* oviduct.
40 Ovary.
41 40
42 39
43 38
44 36
45 28—26—29—38—36—39. (4) Deduct 1 mark for each omission, wrong order or error.
46 Maternal blood capillaries (vessels).
47 Embryo blood capillaries (vessels).
48 Amniotic fluid (fluid).
49 Umbilical cord.
50 Embryo.
51 Uterus wall.
52 Foetal membrane *or* amniotic membrane.
53 Cervix.
54 Placenta.
55 Artery/vein (blood vessels). (2)
56 Oxygen/food *or* named examples of food. (2)
57 Carbon dioxide/waste *or* named examples e.g. urea. (2)
58 Diffusion.
59 Blood circulation *or* flow, *or* blood pumped.
60 Protection.
61 Muscle contraction *or* uterus contraction.
62 The cut umbilical cord.
63 Surgical removal of the baby through the wall of the abdomen.
64 Baby's head near cervix/ uterus contraction *or* dilated cervix/breaking of waters *or* loss of fluid. Any 2 (2)
65 Plenty of calcium in her diet.
66 15th–19th October.*
67 27th–31st October.*
68 23rd–29th October.*
69 27th October–3rd November.*
70 4th November–9th November.*
71 The progesterone level would remain high after 4th November.*
72 26th–30th October.*
*Allow + or — 1 day in each case.
73 Syphilis/Gonorrhea/N.S.U. (2)
74 Bacteria.
75 Sexual intercourse (copulation).
76 Reproductive organs *or* named reproductive organs.
77 Passed from mother to foetus during pregnancy.
78 E
79 H
80 A
81 I
82 C
83 D
84 F
85 J
86 B
87 G
88 and 89 Any two from: growth of beard/voice breaking/ pubic hair/become more muscular. (2)
90 and 91 Any two from: mammary glands develop/hips etc widen/growth of pubic hair/ subcutaneous fat depostion/ menstruation starts. (2)

Total 99

Chapter 12 Inheritance and Population

1 C
2 C
3 D
4 D
5 A
6 D
7 A
8 C
9 D
10 C

Several reversals of the answers can occur in 11–30 and 31–48 depending upon the candidate's layout. The way to mark is to copy these answers onto a copy of the questions and then compare with the candidate's answers.

11 Curl × non-curl.
12 Curl × curl.
13 Cc.
14 cc.
15 Cc.
16 Cc.
17 C and c.
18 c.
19 C and c.
20 C and c.
21 Cc
22 cc
23 CC
24 Cc
25 cC
26 cc.
27 Curl.
28 Non-curl.
29 3 curl.
30 1 non-curl.
31 Tt.
32 tt.
33 TT.
34 tt.
35 Tt.
36 Tt.
37 T
38 t
39 T
40 t
41 TT.
42 Tt.
43 tT.
44 tt.
45 Taster.
46 Taster.
47 Taster.
48 Non-taster.
49 Avoid exposure to sunlight to avoid burning/Avoid bright light which would hurt their eyes. (2)
50 A ratio of 1 albino child to 3 normal *or* $\frac{1}{4}$ albino.
51 All normal children.
52 Half normal and half albino children *or* 50:50.
53 $60 \times 60 = 3600$ i.e. one in 3600.
54 $4 \times 3600 = 14\,400$ i.e. one in 14 400 .
55 Since they carry the recessive gene they should check that albinos do not occur in the relatives of their future marriage partners.
56 None.
57 AA, AO.
58 Group A.
59 BB, BO, OO.
60 Groups B and O.
61 AA, AB, AO, BO.
62 Groups A, B and AB.
63 AB, AO, BO, OO.
64 Groups A, B, AB and O.
65 A
66 b
67 Mixes.
68 Agglutination.
69 Agglutination.
70 Mixes.
71 B
72 a
73 Agglutination.
74 Mixes.
75 Agglutination.
76 Mixes.
77 A and B.
78 None.
79 Mixes.
80 Mixes.
81 Mixes.
82 Mixes.
83 None.
84 a and b.
85 Agglutination.
86 Agglutination.
87 Agglutination.
88 Mixes.
89 dd dwarf female.
90 Dd normal male.
91 dd dwarf male.
92 Dd normal female.
93 dd dwarf female.
94 Dd normal male.
95 Dd normal female
96 A dwarf is unlikely to marry into a family whose relatives have the dwarf condition *or* chance too great for all these carriers to come together in the same family.
97 The gene for colour blindness is present on the sex chromosome.
98 The gene is on the X chromosome/males only have one X chromosome so this phenotype is expressed, unlike females where a second gene on the other chromosome will mask its effect. (2)
99 A person carrying a recessive gene/which is not expressed in the phenotype. (Same for disease carried but not shown) (2)
100 (i) Female (ii) Cc (iii) colour vision (3).
101 (i) male (ii) C– (iii) colour vision. (3)
102 (i) female (ii) cc (iii) colour blind. (3)
103 (i) male (ii) c– (iii) colour blind. (3)

104 H
105 G
106 A
107 E
108 D
109 B
110 C
111 I
112 F
113 Age composition histogram *or* bar chart.
114 50+55+5 thousand= 110 000.
115 55+60+15 thousand= 130 000.
116 110 000+130 000= 240 000.
117 Number of births in the year=240×4·5=1080/ -1
Numbers of deaths in the year= 240×3·5=840/ -1
Population increase= 1080—840=240/ -1
Total population at the end of the year=240 000+240
=240 240/ -1 (4)
118 Crude birth rate=

$$\frac{\text{Live births} \times 1000}{\text{Total population}} = \frac{1080 \times 1000}{240\,000} / = 4{\cdot}5 \text{ (2) *}$$

119 Crude death rate=

$$\frac{\text{Deaths} \times 1000}{\text{Total population}} = \frac{840 \times 1000}{240\,000} / = 3{\cdot}5 \text{ (2) *}$$

120 4·5—3·5=1·0
121 Fertility rate=

$$\frac{\text{Live births} \times 1000}{\text{Total women aged 15–44}} = \frac{1080 \times 1000}{60\,000} / = 18{\cdot}0 \text{ (2)}$$

122 Expanding.
123 High fertility rate *or* high birth rate *or* large number of fertile females, *or* few people over 44.
124 Increased death rates (or wars) *or* migration *or* disease.
125 Males have higher death rate *or* are less hardy *or* go to war etc.
126 Birth control practised *or* living standards rise.

Total 142

* Answers can be read directly from histograms.

Chapter 13 Disease Organisms and their Control

1 B
2 B
3 A
4 C
5 A
6 C
7 C
8 A
9 A
10 B
11 Tapeworm.
12 Flea.
13 Louse.
14 Small intestine.
15 Hooks/suckers. (2)
16 Intestines *or* in faeces.
17 Skin *or* hair.
18 Claws.
19 On skin *or* clothes *or* on rats.
20 Hair.
21 Claws.
22 On hair *or* in dirt.
23 Typhus/plague. (2)
24 Typhus/relapsing fever. (2)
25 Hunger/become thin *or* undernourished. (2)
26 Organisms/living in or on another organism (the host)/ from which nutrient is obtained, leading to the disadvantage or death of the host.
(3)
27 F
28 J
29 H
30 G
31 B
32 C
33 I
34 E
35 A
36 D
37 Origin of living organisms from non living matter.
38 A. broth *or* nutrient/

B. swan neck *or* delivery tube. (2)
39 trap micro-organisms.
40 Control/without bung or tube. (2)
41 To sterilise *or* destroy all organisms.
42 A or broth remains fresh/ control goes bad *or* micro-organisms develop. (2)
43 Nothing *or* no growth.
44 Growth of micro-organisms.
45 Micro-organisms are in *or* carried in the air, *or* boiling can destroy micro-organisms.
46 Bacterial growth.
47 C and D.
48 0·05% or C.
49 A and B would not kill the bacteria/D would burn the wound. (2)
50 Lister.
51 Aseptic methods.
52 Enzymes inactivated *or* metabolism slowed (too cold).
53 40–45°C.
54 Enzymes destroyed *or* protoplasm destroyed.
55 As bacteria increase in size they divide *or* rate of division indicates rate of growth.
56 Optimum temperature is 40–45°C *or* greatest activity near body temperature.
57 A colony of bacteria which neither increases or decreases in size *or* static in growth.
58 Petri.
59 Incubator *or* pressure cooker/6·8 kg for 10 minutes minimum. (2)
60 Nichrome wire *or* loop/ flamed/in culture and streaked. (3)
61 40 to 45°C.
62 Koch.
63 Prevent accidental infection *or* methods described.
64 Typhoid.
65 *Pneumococcus.*
66 *Pneumococcus* colony reduced in extent/as penicillin diffuses in *or Pneumococcus* grows/as resistant forms develop. (2)
67 Bacterial organisms causing yaws *or* syphilis *or* gon orrhoea *or* T.B. etc.
68 Fungal growth.
69 Typhoid is rod shaped/ pneumococcus is spherical in shape. (2)
70 100.
71 2000 or 2×10^3.
72 2 000 000 or $2\times10.^6$
73 Time taken for development of enzymes *or* absorption of water.
74 Reduction in nutrient materials/ accumulation of waste products of metabolism. (2)
75 Sugar *or* carbohydrate.
76 Carbon dioxide.
77 Turn lime water milky *or* use bicarbonate indicator which turns yellow.
78 Alcohol *or* energy.
79 Fungus.
80 Bread making *or* alcoholic drinks.
81 Anti-serum *or* serum *or* diphtheria antibodies.
82 Vaccine *or* attenuated antigens.
83 Individual B produces antibodies.
84 Passive.
85 Cells have to process the antigens first *or* manufacturing cells will have to be made.
86 Plasma cells *or* lymphocytes.
87 Destroy antigens *or* clump antigens.
88 A person suffering from diphtheria *or* in contact with the disease.
89 Within the body of another animal and then extracted.
90 Diphtheria toxin weakened by application of heat and then treated with formalin (formaldehyde).
91 Booster

Total 107

CHAPTER 14 Disease and its Transmission

Disease	Organism	Enter body	Symptoms
Cholera	**1** bacterium	**2** food	**3** diarrhoea
Diphtheria	**4** bacterium	**5** air	**6** throat inflammation
Dysentery	**7** protozoan bacterium	**8** food	**9** diarrhoea
Filariasis	**10** helminth	**11** insect bite	**12** swollen lymph glands
Hookworm	**13** helminth	**14** skin in water	**15** anaemia
Influenza	**16** virus	**17** air	
Leprosy	**18** bacterium	**19** contact	**20** sores
Leptospirosis	**21** bacterium	**22** skin in water	**23** yellow skin
Malaria	**24** protozoan	**25** insect bite	**26** anaemia
Ringworm	**27** fungus	**28** contact	**29** red patch
Roundworm	**30** helminth	**31** food	
Schistosomiasis	**32** helminth	**33** skin in water	**34** blood in faeces
Sleeping sickness	**35** protozoan	**36** insect bite	**37** swollen lymph glands
Smallpox	**38** virus	**39** contact *or* air	**40** red spots, sores
Tuberculosis	**41** bacterium	**42** air *or* food	**43** coughing
Typhoid	**44** bacterium	**45** food	**46** diarrhoea
Venereal disease	**47** bacterium	**48** contact	**49** red spots, sores
Whooping cough	**50** bacterium	**51** air	**52** coughing
Yaws	**53** bacterium	**54** contact	**55** red spots, sores
Yellow fever	**56** virus	**57** insect bite	**58** yellow skin

59 A
60 C (D)
61 C
62 C
63 C
64 D
65 D
66 A
67 D
68 D
69 *Trypanosoma.*
70 Blood.
71 Flagellum.
72 Sleeping sickness.
73 Damages the part of the brain controlling sleeping rhythm.
74 Inject drugs into veins *or* inject Pentamidine.
75 Does not destroy parasites in the central nervous system.
76 Tsetse fly *or Glossina.*
77 In the salivary glands.
78 In the soil *or* ground.
79 They provide a reservoir of the parasites *or* parasites live in animals.
80 Malaria.
81 *Plasmodium.*
82 Daraprim *or* Paludrine (*or* Plasmoquine *or* Chloroquine *or* Mepacrine *or* Quinine).
83 Toxins released by the parasite/when the red cells burst. (2)
84 Damage to the red cells.
85 Destroy the anopheline mosquitoes.
86 Examine blood smear for parasites.
87 In the mosquito.
88 Disease seldom kills.
89 Mosquito larvae sink/die due to oxygen lack. (2)
90 Fish eat the mosquito larvae.
91 Prevents mosquito biting

them and carrying the parasite to others.
92 Cholera.
93 lobed-mouthparts.
94 Remove rubbish.
95 Malaria.
96 Body settles at 30° to skin.
97 Any from—spray oil on water, stock water with fish, remove stagnant water.
98 Yellow fever.
99 White stripes.
100 See 97.
101 Filariasis.
102 Body settles parallel to skin.
103 See 97.

Total 105

Chapter 15 Social Hygiene

1 A
2 A
3 B
4 C
5 A
6 A
7 D
8 B
9 B
10 D
11 B
12 B
13 A
14 D
15 B
16 Prevailing wind blows smells from the refuse tip *or* sewage works across the town.
Sewage works too close to wells.
Sewage works *or* refuse tips too close to houses.
Crowded housing.
Housing too near swamps *or* on low land.
Sewage effluent has to pass by houses *or* works too far from the river.
Factories too near housing etc.
(Other answers acceptable.)
1 mark each to 5 (5)
17 In the nearby well.
18 Incubate a water sample on an agar plate *or* bacteriological method described
19 Close the well etc/ quarantine all patients/ closely observe *or* quarantine all contacts/report the disease/ active immunisation of all inhabitants etc. Any 3 (3)
20 Medical Officer of Health/ M.O.H. *or* other named official.
21 Near swamps where mosquitoes breed.
22 Drain the swamps./ Quarantine all cases *or* screen under nets/destroy mosquitoes by sprays/kill larva by oil on water/stocking with fish etc. Any 3. (3)
23 High humidity prevents evaporation of sweat.
24 On the hills/better drainage *or* more breeze etc. (2)
25 Fans/air conditioning/air bricks/louvred windows/more windows/roof vent. Any 3 (3)
26 Place for sandfleas to breed spreading chigger *or* lice *or* ticks *or* not easy to clean *or* damp.
27 Rising damp, promotes more fungal growth.
28 May be eaten by termites *or* wood worm.
29 Lack of insulation *or* causes overheating *or* damp.
30 Absorbs too much heat *or* does not reflect sunlight.
31 Lack of ventilation *or* reduces convection currents.
32 Reduces convection *or* ventilation.
33 11 per 100 000.
34 Week 10.
35 Sulphur dioxide.
36 No apparent relationship at this concentration.
37 High smoke concentration increases the death rate/because more deaths follow after the higher concentrations are are recorded. (2)
38 Grammes per cubic metre/ parts per million. (2)
39 Weaker individuals who could normally have died in this period will have died earlier due to the high concentration of smoke.
40 Respiratory ailments/e.g. bronchitis/lung cancer/ asthma/ silicosis. Any 2 (2)

41 Coal miners likely to be suffering from silicosis.
42 Heavy smokers likely to be suffering from lung cancer *or* bronchitis.
43 Large urban area.
44 *Glossina* and *Culex*.
45 *Anopheles* only.
46 *Anopheles* and *Culex*.
47 Viruses not visible under a microscope.
48 Life cycle of *Glossina* takes less than 3 months so they cannot transmit the disease.
49 Yes, because they are also reservoirs for Trypanosomes.
50 The U-bend seals to prevent the escape of gases.
51 Carry sewage.
52 Separates paper *or* sticks etc from the crude sewage.
53 The grit pit allows heavy particles to settle.
54 Sedimentation *or* settling of solids to form sludge.
55 Where the sludge is stored and bacteria decompose it.
56 Effluent is sprinkled onto the coke beds for aeration.
57 Coke beds contain the organisms to decompose the sewage.
58 Humus tank is where further solids settle after filtering.
59 Nearby rivers carry away the effluent.
60 T
61 S
62 F
63 F
64 S
65 S
66 F
67 S
68 T
69 T
70 F

2 marks for the name of the prison with one reason.

	Prison	Reason
71	C	Beri-beri caused by lack of vitamin B_1 not present in milled rice. (2)
72	B	Dysentery caused by contaminated food. (2)
73	C	Liver flukes transmitted in uncooked fish. (2)
74	B	Scabies transmitted by contaminated bedding. (2)
75	A	Because of the high incidence of bronchitis or lung cancer. (2)
76	A	High incidence of lung cancer or coronary thrombosis. (2)
77	B	Yellow fever most common. (2)
78	A	Because of the high level of coronary thrombosis. (2)
79	A	Because of the high incidence of T.B. and bronchitis. (2)
80	B	Because of hookworm infections. (2)
81	B	Yellow fever transmitted by mosquitoes. (2)
82	A	Because of high incidence of T.B. and bronchitis. (2)

83

Disease	Prison	Prophylaxis
Hookworm	B	Prevent contact with water *or* proper faeces disposal *or* method of avoiding water described.
Dysentery	B	Clean kitchens *or* food preparation *or* look for carriers.
Beri-beri	C	Provide vitamin B_1 *or* stop milling rice.
Yellow fever	B	Destroy mosquitoes.
Bronchitis	A/B	Stop smoking *or* prevent air pollution, improve ventilation.
Scabies	B	Clean and change bedding *or* destroy mites.
Tuberculosis	A	Improve ventilation or avoid overcrowding.
Lung Cancer	A	Stop smoking *or* prevent air pollution *or* X-ray examination.
Liver fluke	C	Cook fish thoroughly *or* proper faeces disposal.
Coronary thrombosis	A/B	Give plenty of exercise *or* stop smoking.

Allow 1 mark for any *one* prophylactic measure mentioned for each prison correctly named. Total (10).

Total 118

Essay Question Mark Schemes

17

The following examples are to help teachers to construct mark schemes so that they may more accurately mark internal examination papers. They will also serve to show candidates the importance of facts rather than irrelevant descriptions in answers. Such schemes need flexibility in interpretation particularly in allowing marks for phrases with similar meanings.

Question: With the aid of a large labelled diagram describe the function of the parts of the eye.

Mark scheme:

Labels. Optic nerve, blind spot, choroid, sclerotic, retina, fovea *or* yellow spot, cornea, conjunctiva, ciliary muscle, suspensory ligament, lens, iris, pupil, aqueous humour *or* anterior chamber, vitreous humour *or* posterior chamber, extrinsic eye muscles

$16 \times \frac{1}{2} = 8$

(Allow ½ mark for each part correctly labelled if the shape is reasonable. Deduct 1 or 2 marks for poor quality drawings)

Functions:

Conjunctiva—protects by preventing entry of grit etc.	1
Cornea—refracts light	1
Suspensory ligament—supports the lens.	1
Lens—focusses light/by changing shape	2
Ciliary muscle—accommodation/explanation	2
Iris—controls intensity of light entering/method	2
Aqueous humour—refracts light *or* provides shape or support	1
Vitreous humour—refracts light *or* provides shape or support	1
Fovea—good resolution/cones/colour vision	2
Retina—light induces nerve impulse (transduction)	2
rods/low light intensity	2
Sub total	17
Total	25

(The above facts should be well presented in sentence form to gain marks.)

Question: What is an enzyme? Outline the properties of enzymes. Describe an experiment to illustrate the effect of temperature on salivary amylase.

Mark scheme:

What is an enzyme? Chemical *or* protein/made by living cells/acts like a catalyst/on a substrate/speeds up the rate of reaction/small quantities chemically change large quantities/ intra and extra cellular action/named according to the substrate on which it acts. 8

Properties:

Optimum pH activity/optimum temperature activity/specific to substrate/destroyed at high temperatures/reaction rate depends on the substrate and product concentration 5

(*Allow the above facts under either heading once*) Total 13

Experiment:

Method of collecting salivary amylase	1
control with water	1
addition of 1% starch solution	1
water bath at various temperatures	1
samples tested with iodine/red→blue black	2
results — rate increases with increased temperature	1
fall off at 50°C	1
graph of results	1
enzyme inactivated at high temperatures	1
	10
Bonus 1 or 2 for **good** descriptions	2
Total	25